WORKSHOP PROCESSES
FOR MECHANICAL ENGINEERING TECHNICIANS

VOLUME I

GENERAL TECHNICAL SERIES

General Editor:

AIR COMMODORE J. R. MORGAN,
O.B.E., B.Sc. (Eng.), M.I.Mech.E., F.R.Ae.S., R.A.F.
Formerly
Director of Studies
Royal Air Force Technical College
and
Deputy Director, Educational Services, Air Ministry.

Radio
(in three volumes)
J. D. TUCKER,
A.M.Brit.I.R.E.
and
D. F. WILKINSON,
B.Sc. (Eng.), ,A.M.I.E.E.

Mathematics for Telecommunications
and Electrical Engineering
(in two volumes)
W. H. GRINSTED,
O.B.E., M.I.E.E., F.C.G.I.
and
D. F. SPOONER,
B.Sc. (Lond.)

Engineering Science and Calculations
(in three volumes)
W. E. FISHER,
O.B.E., D.Sc., A.M.I.Mech.E.

The Principles of
Telecommunications Engineering
Volume I
(Volume 2 in preparation)
H. R. HARBOTTLE,
O.B.E., B.Sc. (Eng.), D.F.H., M.I.E.E.
and
B. L. G. HANMAN,
B.Sc. (Eng.)

Elementary Telecommunication Practice
J. R. G. SMITH,
A.M.I.E.E.

Simplified Calculus
F. L. WESTWATER,
O.B.E., R.N. (Ret'd.), M.A. (Edin.), M.A. (Cantab.), A.M.I.E.E.

Engineering Drawing and Materials
for Mechanical Engineering Technicians
H. ORD,
A.R.Ae.S., F.R.Econ.S.

Engineering Drawing for G1 and G2 Courses
H. ORD,
A.R.Ae.S. F.R.Econ.S.

WORKSHOP PROCESSES

FOR

MECHANICAL ENGINEERING TECHNICIANS

VOLUME I

R. T. PRITCHARD

A.M.I.Prod.E., Full Tech. Cert. C.G.L.I.,
Teacher's Cert. in Metalwork

Lecturer in Mechanical Engineering,
Garretts Green Technical College, Birmingham.
Examiner for the City and Guilds of London Institute,
The Union of Educational Institutions and
The Welsh Joint Education Committee

THE ENGLISH UNIVERSITIES PRESS LTD

102 NEWGATE STREET
LONDON E.C.1

First Printed 1963

*Printed in Great Britain for The English Universities Press Limited
by Elliott Bros. & Yeoman Ltd., Speke, Liverpool*

Editor's Foreword

THE new awareness of the imperative need to make the very most of our technical potential makes a foreword to the General Technical Series almost unnecessary, for it aims directly at encouraging young men—and women—to extend their interests, widen their knowledge and improve their technical skills.

The City and Guilds of London Institute makes special provision for the technican to acquire a qualification appropriate to his Craft. The wide range of examinations now held under its auspices is ample evidence not merely of the need to cater for the technician but also of the growing desire of the Craftsman to improve his knowledge of his Craft. Many of the books in the present series will be related to syllabuses of the City and Guilds of London Institute, but this will not limit their use merely to preparation for the examinations held by that body. The aim is to encourage students to study those technical subjects which are closely related to their daily work and, by so doing, to obtain a better understanding of basic principles. Any study of this kind cannot fail to stimulate interest in the subject and should produce a technician with a clearer understanding of what he is doing and how it should best be done.

But although the series is intended to appeal, in the first instance, to students who are interested in the certificates offered by the City and Guilds of London Institute that must be regarded as only the immediate aim. Those students who, as a result of their initial endeavours, find that they are capable of going further should aim at obtaining either a National Certificate in an appropriate field of engineering or, alternatively, a General Certificate of Education at a level appropriate to their potential attainment.

All the books in the series will be written by experienced and well qualified teachers who are thoroughly conversant with the problems encountered by young men and women in studying the subject with which their books deal.

J. R. M.

Author's Preface

I HAVE, in writing and illustrating this introductory volume, attempted to provide a much needed link between teacher and student. Workshop Processes is not the easiest of subjects to teach, for much of it is descriptive and outside the immediate experience of the sixteen year old apprentice. Because of this, there is a real danger of the student having, as his main pre-occupation, the problem of keeping pace with the volume of blackboard work, absorbing little or nothing of the lesson content.

If we, as a Nation, are to meet the impending challenge of Continental manufacturing skills, then there is little doubt that the supply of skilled technicians and craftsmen must be of the highest possible quality and quantity.

I have, then, intended this volume as a class book. The first five chapters lead up to the principles and techniques involved in good class bench work, and no opportunity has been lost of impressing students with the need for care, patience and skill, without which accurate well-finished work cannot be produced. The last five chapters introduce the student to the machine tool aspect of Workshop Processes, with emphasis placed on the principles underlying the production of the surfaces required in engineering manufacture.

I have also attempted to keep the written text to a minimum and to balance this by providing ample illustrations; not of actual tools or components, but of the principles and techniques involved. The object of this is twofold. Firstly, the student age-group will be sixteen plus, and a greater impact can be achieved with an illustration. Secondly, by keeping the text at a minimum, considerable supplementation is possible by the class teacher, and this may well take the form of class notes.

Each chapter will require about three to four weeks of class work, and basic questions are provided at the end of each chapter. The answering of some of these questions could well take up the last half hour of class time, whilst a selection could be set for homework.

Ideally, then, every student has this volume, and is guided through the ten chapters by an able and understanding teacher. If, in this way, the young apprentice is assisted in completing successfully the first year of his studies for technician status, then the writing of this introductory volume has been worthwhile.

Finally, I should like to thank Brian G. Staples, M.A., F.L.A., for reading the proofs.

R. T. Pritchard

Sutton Coldfield

CONTENTS

Introduction

FIG. 1 shows an engineering assembly which can be instantly recognised. Although it is only a part of the humble bicycle, it is a good example of the many engineering skills which are called upon to produce this assembly.

Before embarking upon a course of study, it is as well to have clearly

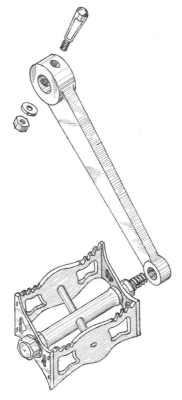

FIG. 1.—PEDAL AND CRANK ASSEMBLY.

xi

defined, not only the necessity for the course, but also the reasons for the choice and presentation order of the subject matter.

This simple assembly will serve as an example to illustrate the essential knowledge required by those who aspire to gain technician status in the engineering industry, and also as an introduction to the subject matter which forms the chapters of this book.

What are the problems, and decisions to be made before manufacturing the separate components which make up this assembly?

Whilst it is well within the capacity of a skilled man to produce these parts individually, such a method would be utterly impracticable, due to the time required and excessive final cost if, say, 10,000 assemblies were required per month. For production figures of this kind, the parts must be mass produced, using the most economical methods available, whilst ensuring that the completed assembly will give many years of reliable and trouble-free service. Many processes and techniques will be involved, and these can now be listed in their order of presentation.

Materials

A closer study of the assembly will reveal that all the parts are made from steel. There are very good reasons why steel has been chosen, and the first chapter will be concerned with the origin and manufacture of ferrous metals, of which steel forms an important group. Engineers use a large number of different metals, but ten times more steel is consumed than the total amount of all other metals. This means that a closer look at the manufacture of steel is worthwhile and necessary, if the use of this material is to be put to the best advantage.

Heat Treatment

It is possible, by using the correct heat treatment process, to modify or improve a steel component, thus making it more suitable for the kind of work it has to do. For example, the links of a bicycle chain are subject to a great deal of wear and also strong tensional forces. To resist the wear and abrasion, the links should be hard, but such a chain would also be brittle and liable to break. By means of a suitable heat treatment process it is possible to produce a chain which possesses hard wearing surfaces and yet is strong enough to withstand even excessive loads.

The chapter on heat treatment will serve as an introduction to the basic heat treatment processes.

The Joining of Metals

It would take some time to count the number of components which, when assembled, make a complete bicycle. The steel tubes must be joined together to make the frame. The chain is composed of a very large number of separate links, rollers and rivets. The wheels are complicated structures, and provision must be made for adjustment of handle bar and saddle height.

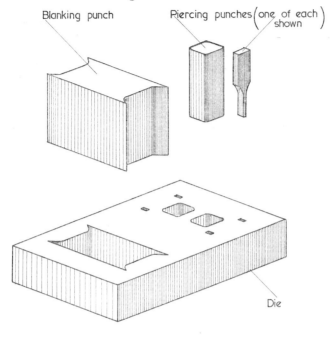

Blanking punch   Piercing punches (one of each shown)

Die

Punches clear die by ·0015"

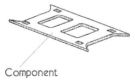

Component

FIG. 2.—PUNCHES AND DIE USED IN A PRESS TOOL.

All these components must be joined together in one way or another and there are many devices in use. It is evident, then, that the joining of metals is of great concern to the engineer. Chapter 3 deals with the basic principles and techniques in general use.

Measurement

Reference to fig. 1 will show the need for measurement in engineering.

The crank must be a good fit on the spindle, the taper of the cotter pin must mate with the taper in the crank. The hexagonal nut must screw on to the cotter pin, yet not be too slack. These are but a few examples of the necessity of accurate measurement if the bicycle is to have a long and useful life.

The chapter on measurement will serve as an introduction to the basic principles underlying the technique of measurement.

Metal Removal at the Bench

Whilst the majority of components are produced by mass production methods, it must not be thought that bench work is now obsolete.

Fig. 2 shows punches and a die which, when aligned in a press tool, will produce several hundred thousand of the pedal parts shown. It will be evident that the punches and die may well be hand made, and this class of work calls for a very high degree of skill and precision. Much of this work is carried out at the bench, and the resultant work depends largely on the ability and skill of the craftsman.

Such work is expensive but the skill of the craftsman now goes to produce the **capital goods** such as press tools, machine tools, jigs, fixtures and gauges, and the combination of this equipment enables the engineering industry to mass produce components at a rapid and economic rate.

Machine Tools

Machine tools are the producers of industry, and a very wide variety of types are in use, capable of producing safety pins or cylinder blocks. Complex though they may be they all perform a similar operation, and that is to produce a given geometrical surface within certain limits of accuracy.

The centre lathe is the mother of the machine tool industry, and the purpose of Chapter 6 is to introduce the student to the fundamentals of machine tools.

The centre lathe, drilling and shaping machine will be dealt with, and particular emphasis will be placed on the geometrical principles involved, and how these principles are utilised in a practical engineering manner. At the present time most machine tools remove metal whilst producing the desired geometrical surface, and this perhaps is a sad reflection on our skill as engineers. A great deal of money and time has been expended by the steel manufacturing industries in producing bars of varying diameter. These bars are then machined on machine tools and the metal removed as swarf. Such a procedure is evidently wasteful, and many new developments can be expected to replace the present method of machining. However, if the secondary purpose of a machine tool is to remove metal, then cutting tools must be used, and a chapter is devoted to the principles and applications of single-point cutting tools.

It may now be appreciated that the term Mechanical Engineering covers a very wide field but, by separating the fundamental principles and putting them into chapter form, it is possible to break down the whole into smaller portions, and then rebuild our knowledge step by step.

In this way we shall see how the limitations of one material or process inevitably lead to the introduction or development of another. Because of this, the engineering industry is in a constant state of development and expansion, but the same basic principles usually remain unaltered.

1 The Manufacture of Ferrous Metals

AT the present time we live in a steel age. The total amount of all other metals used in our manufacturing industries is only one tenth of the amount of steel. This is due to various factors, some of which are:

   (i) Steel is a relatively cheap metal.
  (ii) It is available in a wide range of shapes and sizes.
 (iii) Many different types of steels are obtainable.
 (iv) It possesses both strength and ductility.
  (v) It can be heat treated to improve its properties.
 (vi) It is readily machined.

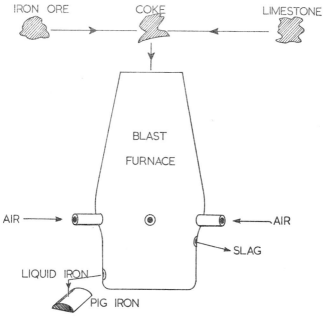

FIG. 3.—THE MANUFACTURE OF PIG IRON.

I

Steel is called a ferrous metal because it contains iron; the Latin name for iron is ferrum, whilst the chemical name for iron is ferrite. Thus all metals which contain iron are called ferrous, and those which have no iron, non-ferrous.

In order to appreciate the difference between iron and steel, it is necessary to have some knowledge of their manufacture, and fig. 3 is a simple line diagram outlining the first stage of iron and steel manufacture.

Manufacture of Pig Iron

It will be seen from the diagram that iron ore, coke and limestone are fed into the container called a blast furnace. Modern blast furnaces are about 100 feet tall and 28 feet in diameter, and are capable of producing 1,500 tons of pig iron every 24 hours. Before considering the process in greater detail let us take a closer look at the materials fed into the furnace, often called the **charge.**

Iron Ore

This forms about 1/20 of the earth's crust and is a sort of earth or rock containing iron. The percentage of iron may vary from 20% to 70%, and the whole purpose of the blast furnace is to separate the iron from the oxides and impurities present in the iron ore.

Coke

Heat is required to separate the iron, and the coke provides the fuel. It is important to note that coke is a form of carbon.

Limestone

The impurities in the iron ore must be removed from the furnace. This is done by making them join with the molten limestone; the limestone also has an important role in removing sulphur from the iron. The presence of any sulphur will make the iron weak and brittle and of no value to engineers.

Air

Air or atmosphere contains about one fifth oxygen and this unites with the coke (carbon) and generates great heat. Modern blast furnaces have hot air blown into them to increase their efficiency. The simple equation given below shows the changes taking place in a blast furnace:

$$IRON\ OXIDE + CARBON = IRON + CARBON\ OXIDES$$
or
$$ORE + COKE = IRON + GAS$$

The Blast Furnace

Fig. 4 shows a section through an early type of blast furnace. It has been chosen because of its simplicity and because the principles which it demonstrates apply to the more complicated blast furnaces now being built. The hot air is blown into the furnace through large ducts called the tuyeres. The coke burns fiercely raising the temperature within the furnace to about 1150° C.

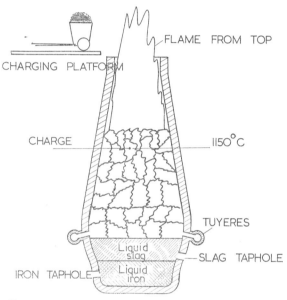

FIG. 4.—SECTION THROUGH A PRIMITIVE BLAST FURNACE.

At this point the iron begins to melt out of the ore, forming droplets which, by reason of their weight, slowly make their way to the bottom of the furnace. At the same time the limestone melts and forms a pool on top of the liquid iron. The remainder of the ore, which is not iron, now joins with the liquid limestone to form slag. This, of course, is only a brief picture of what happens within a blast furnace, because we must remember that there is a chemical reaction also taking place which may be summarised as follows:

(i) The coke burns with the oxygen to produce carbon monoxide.
i.e. CARBON+OXYGEN = CARBON MONOXIDE.

(ii) This gas carbon monoxide attracts oxygen from the iron oxide, producing the gas carbon dioxide and leaving iron;

i.e. IRON OXIDE+CARBON MONOXIDE = IRON+ CARBON DIOXIDE

(iii) This carbon dioxide, as it passes through the coke, reacts once more with the carbon in the coke and turns into carbon monoxide once again, and proceeds to extract the oxygen from the iron ore. Thus the cycle is repeated as the gas proceeds up the furnace.

As the level of liquid iron and slag rises, the time comes when they must be removed from the furnace. First the tap hole for the slag is opened, and the slag runs out. It is possible to treat this slag and turn it into a material suitable for road making, but in most cases it is a waste product.

When the slag is removed the iron is then tapped. This is always a great moment for the men who operate the furnace, and the spectacle of the liquid white-hot iron as it runs from the furnace is a sight not likely to be forgotten. A blast furnace, once lighted, burns continuously and is kept charged with iron-ore, coke and limestone until such time as the furnace linings have to be renewed. It may take as long as a fortnight to re-light a blast furnace and bring it up to the right temperature to deal with a full charge.

In their passage down the furnace, the liquid droplets of iron absorb carbon from the coke, and although the percentage of carbon is only about 3-4%, it is this carbon which gives the iron its extreme fluidity.

This is an important point and worth remembering. The liquid iron may now be taken direct to the steelworks whilst still molten, or cast into pigs. These pigs are about $4'' \times 4''$ of D section, and about 40 inches long. They may be cast automatically in a pig casting machine, or in simple sand beds.

Cast Iron

Engineers have no practical use for pig iron. Its composition is doubtful and it needs a **refining** process. This is carried out in a miniature blast furnace called a **cupola**. Thus the purpose of a cupola is to convert pig iron into cast iron.

The Cupola

We have seen that the blast furnace maintains a continuous smelting process until the furnace linings have to be renewed. Although, in effect, the cupola is a kind of miniature blast furnace it is intermittent in its operation for the firebrick lining wears away quickly and has to be renewed frequently.

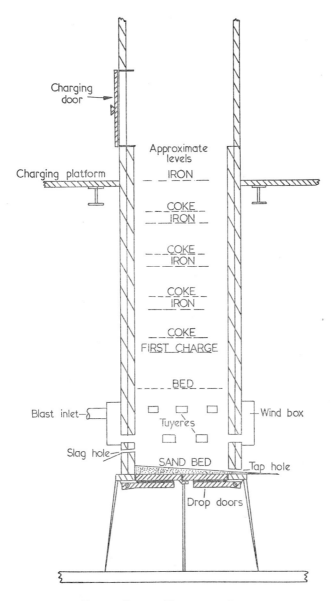

Charging door

Charging platform

Approximate levels

IRON

COKE
IRON

COKE
IRON

COKE
IRON

COKE
FIRST CHARGE

BED

Blast inlet

Wind box

Tuyeres

Slag hole

SAND BED

Tap hole

Drop doors

Fig. 5.—Section Through a Cupola.

According to the quality of the cast iron required, pig iron, steel scrap, some limestone and coke are fed into the cupola, and the resultant metal is poured into ladles and used to make a large variety of castings. The liquid cast iron is extremely fluid, and very suitable for pouring into moulds. Fig. 5 illustrates a typical cupola.

The Properties of Cast Iron

Cast iron will contain about $3\frac{1}{2}\%$ carbon, and the presence of this carbon has a profound effect on its properties. If the liquid cast iron is allowed to cool slowly in the moulds, then the carbon will appear as free carbon, or graphite, in the structure of the metal. This graphite has a serious weakening effect similar in many respects to a wooden beam affected by woodworm. Fig. 6 shows a wooden beam so affected, but its external appearance gives no indication of the drastic loss of strength suffered by this beam. If we take a cross section, it will be clearly seen that the beam is honeycombed with a series of small tunnels or cavities. Such a beam would have very little strength.

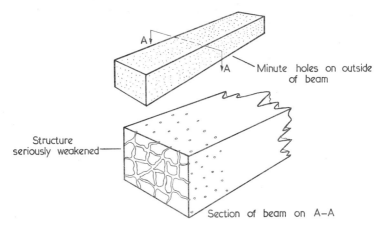

Structure seriously weakened

Minute holes on outside of beam

Section of beam on A–A

FIG. 6.—EFFECT OF WOODWORM ON THE STRENGTH OF A WOODEN BEAM.

The graphite in cast iron has the same effect. Graphite has little or no strength, and its presence within the structure puts a severe limitation on the strength and cold working properties of this metal. Cast iron which is allowed to cool slowly will have a grey appearance when it is fractured or broken, and it is called grey cast iron for this reason. Because the $3\frac{1}{2}\%$ carbon is present as graphite, it cannot be bent or twisted and will not stand up to sudden blows. It breaks without warning because it possesses no spring or elasticity.

This is not a suitable metal for a great many engineering components. Grey cast iron nuts and bolts, spanners, girders, and many other parts would be useless and also dangerous. Yet if the $3\frac{1}{2}\%$ carbon were removed we would be left with pure iron. This is a metal which is fairly strong, easily bent and twisted and, unlike cast iron, easily forged and welded. Such a metal could easily be made into chains, hooks, nails; components which are subjected to sudden shocks and blows.

Wrought Iron

This is the name given to the metal produced by removing the carbon from pig iron. We know that carbon will join with oxygen to form the gases carbon monoxide and carbon dioxide, and this principle is used once again in the manufacture of wrought iron.

Manufacture of Wrought Iron

Fig. 7 is a simple diagram illustrating the principle of a "puddling" furnace, which is the name given to the furnace which produces wrought iron. It will be noted that the heat is reflected from the domed roof onto the charge. This charge consists of pig iron and some mill scale, which is the scale or oxide film which forms on heated steel. When the pig iron melts it is continually stirred, and the carbon is slowly oxidised out. Because carbon gives cast iron its fluidity, the loss of carbon means loss of fluidity, and the molten mass becomes pasty or spongy as a result.

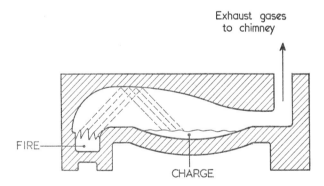

FIG. 7.—PUDDLING OR REVERBERATORY FURNACE.

This spongy iron is now removed from the furnace in much the same way as treacle is removed from a tin, that is, by inserting and revolving a spoon, thus gathering up the treacle.

The wrought iron is then hammered or squeezed to remove as much oxide or slag as possible, which will be present in the iron, then several bars are reheated to white heat, welded together, and then rolled into the required section. Fig. 8 is a line diagram illustrating the process.

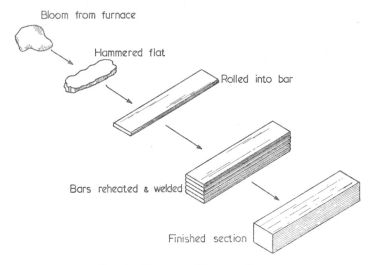

FIG. 8.—PROCESSING WROUGHT IRON.

Properties of Wrought Iron

Wrought iron contains no carbon, but about .05% oxide or slag. This gives to wrought iron a unique property. Because of the processing method, the slag will be directional along the length of the section, and gives wrought iron a fibrous structure. This is very similar to a straight grained wood, say bamboo, and fig. 9 illustrates the behaviour of a wrought iron bar, and a bamboo rod when nicked and bent. The fibrous structure gives wrought iron the ability to stand up to sudden shocks. It is also easily welded and forged, and can be worked in the cold state with little difficulty. It cannot, however, be poured into a mould because it does not become fluid when molten.

Good quality wrought iron, when exposed to the atmosphere, takes on a black film of iron oxide which seems to prevent further oxidisation. Excellent examples of the workability of wrought iron may be seen in the hinges and metal work forming the ornamentation of old cathedrals.

From the brief description of the manufacture of wrought iron given here, it should be clear that this manufacture involves a great deal of manual effort and stress. Blindness at an early age was not uncommon among the master puddlers of a hundred years ago. At this time there was an ever increasing demand for a strong and ductile metal, and this need could only be met by mass production.

It had been found that if the carbon content of the iron could be controlled between 0.1% and 0.5% then a variety of strong metals could be produced. These are mild and medium carbon steels.

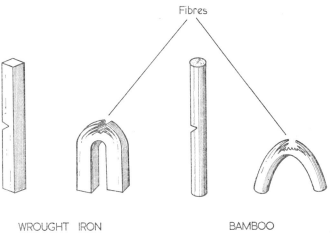

WROUGHT IRON   BAMBOO

Fig. 9.—BENDING TEST OF WROUGHT IRON AND BAMBOO.

The Manufacture of Steel

If the carbon content of iron can be kept within about $1\frac{1}{2}\%$, then the carbon will combine chemically with the iron and will not be present as graphite. For this reason steels are stronger and possess ductility, unlike cast iron. The strength and ductility will depend upon the carbon percentage and, because of this, steels having about 0.2% to 0.5% carbon are widely used.

We have seen that the method employed in the puddling furnace was to oxidise the carbon out of the cast iron by considerable manual effort. In 1856 Henry Bessemer patented his converter, having the brilliant idea of taking air to the molten cast iron, by blowing it through under pressure. Thus the oxygen in the air would combine with the carbon to form carbon monoxide, leaving pure iron. Steel of the required carbon content could then be obtained by adding to the converter a given amount of carbon in the form of ferro-manganese. This process, which could convert up to 30 tons of molten pig iron into steel in 15 minutes, revolutionised the whole of our iron industry.

It brought down the price of steel to one fifth of its former cost, and made available this strong and ductile metal in vast quantities.

Except in certain specialised cases, wrought iron disappeared from the engineering field, assisted in no small measure by the collapse of the celebrated Tay Bridge in 1879. This bridge, considered at the time of its building as an engineering wonder, was constructed of cast iron supports and wrought iron spans. One stormy night as a train was crossing the rear lights of the train were seen to disappear and daylight revealed a large gap in the bridge. A total of 78 lives were lost when the train plunged into the Tay as the bridge collapsed. This disaster would not have happened if the bridge had been constructed from steel, and it brought to an end the use of cast iron and wrought iron as bridge building materials.

The Bessemer Process

The Bessemer converter is a pear-shaped vessel shown in section in fig. 10. It can be tilted by hydraulic means, and fig. 10a shows it receiving a charge of molten pig iron. As it is rotated to an upright position, air at a pressure of about 25 lb. per square inch is turned on. The oxygen in the air combines with the carbon, together with other impurities present, and the temperature of the melt actually rises due to the chemical reactions taking place. Scrap metal may be added if the temperature is considered excessive. At the end of the "BLOW", the Bessemer is tilted back to the horizontal, and ferro-manganese added to give the required carbon content. After testing, the melt is poured into ingot moulds.

The original Bessemer process did not eliminate phosphorus, and high phosphoric ores could not be used, because the presence of phosphorus in steel causes serious embrittlement. This problem was removed by lining the converter with magnesia or dolomite firebricks, which would remove the phosphorus from the iron. Some limestone is also added. Such converters are called "BASIC", whilst the original Bessemer process is called "ACID".

The Open Hearth Process

About 80% of the steel made in Great Britain is produced by the open hearth process, developed by Siemens and Martin. It is similar in principle to a puddling furnace, operating on the reverberatory principle, or the reflection of hot gases from a domed roof. High temperatures are necessary, and a method of heat regeneration is used, whereby the hot exhaust gases pass through and thus heat a chamber. Whilst the incoming gases pass through a similar chamber on the other side of the furnace, which has previously been heated, this chamber loses its heat and the incoming gases are then fed through the hot chamber, whilst the exhaust gases are now made to pass through and reheat the chamber vacated by the incoming gases.

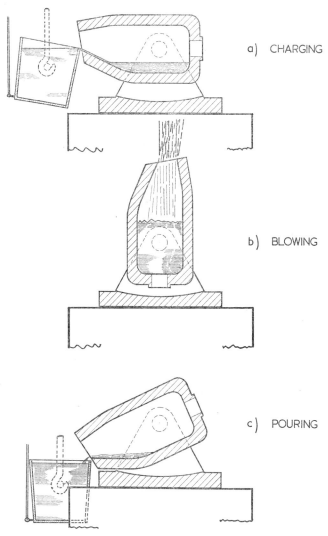

a) CHARGING

b) BLOWING

c) POURING

FIG. 10.—THE BESSEMER PROCESS.

In this way, the inlet and outlet of gas is switched from one chamber to the other, the total effect being to ensure the pre-heat of the incoming

gases before combustion in the furnace. Fig. 11 illustrates the principle
involved, and comparison can be made with the reverberatory furnace
shown in fig. 7, where the exhaust gas is allowed to escape to the atmosphere through the chimney.

It is possible to use up to 50% of scrap steel in the open hearth
process, and when one considers that more iron ore has been taken from
the earth's crust since 1900 than was ever taken before that date, the
use of scrap is an important feature in the manufacture of iron and steel.
Further, the open hearth process allows a better control over the steel
making than is possible with the Bessemer process.

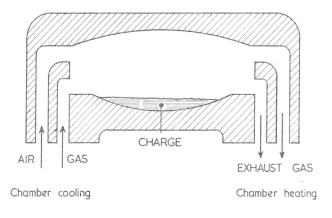

AIR | GAS   EXHAUST GAS

Chamber cooling   Chamber heating

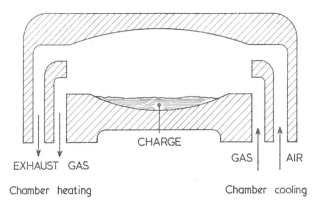

EXHAUST GAS   GAS | AIR

Chamber heating   Chamber cooling

FIG. 11.—THE OPEN HEARTH FURNACE: PRINCIPLE OF REGENERATION.

Cast or Alloy Steels

Reference back to fig. 2 will show the punches and dies used to mass produce the pedal component. The steel used in these punches and dies must be of very high quality, with close control over the alloying elements present. Such steels cannot be produced on a large scale, and small amounts are made at a time. Molten steel tends to absorb some of the gases present in the furnace and thus have impurities. For these reasons high quality steels are made in small crucibles, which isolate the liquid metal from the furnace atmosphere.

Crucible Process

Fig. 12 shows a simple furnace used in the manufacture of crucible steel. The charge, consisting of Swedish iron of high quality and steel blister bars (iron bars heated in charcoal) together with any other elements required in the finished steel, are placed in the crucibles and sealed. Whilst in the furnace this charge melts. Some slag will again form on top of the liquid steel. This is removed before pouring, and

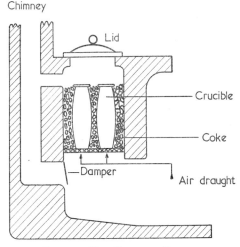

FIG. 12.—THE CRUCIBLE PROCESS.

it is also necessary to add a de-oxidiser (aluminium or manganese) to remove the gases which may be present in the liquid steel. The steel is then poured into ingot moulds and rolled into the required section.

It must be remembered that many furnaces are now electrically heated, and such furnaces possess many advantages over the conventional method of heating by gas or coke.

Summary

We have now covered the basic principles and processes of the manufacture of ferrous metals. Do not be alarmed if you consider this chapter somewhat lengthy or complicated. The history of mankind is often related to the materials used, ranging from the Stone Age to the Iron Age, and it has taken many thousands of years of painful effort to achieve the present techniques and processes.

Over two thousand years ago, iron was being used by the Romans as weapons and tools. Copper has been used by man for over 5,000 years, and lead was extensively used in Roman times for their central heating.

Provided we are familiar with the basic principles involved, each generation of engineers tends to improve on the methods and techniques which are passed on to us, and the story of engineering is like turning over the pages of a book, each succeeding page being an improvement on the previous page.

Perhaps fig. 13 will enable us to retrace our path.

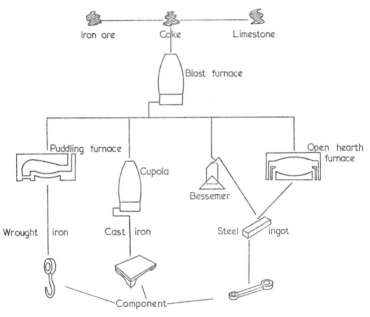

FIG. 13.—LINE DIAGRAM OF FERROUS METAL MANUFACTURE.

Coke, iron ore and limestone enter a blast furnace and pig iron is produced. This pig iron may be refined in a cupola producing cast iron. This is poured into moulds to make castings.

Because of the weakness of cast iron in tension, pig iron can be processed in a puddling furnace to produce wrought iron, which will contain no carbon. But wrought iron is expensive: it is three times the price of mild steel and too ductile or soft for many engineering components. Most of our pig iron, therefore, is turned into mild steel using the Bessemer or open hearth process, where the carbon is removed by oxidisation and a given amount added to bring the steel to the required carbon percentage. The open hearth system is preferred because large quantities of scrap metal can be used.

It will be noted that the product of these steel furnaces is ingots, although steel castings are also produced; mild steel does not possess the fluidity of cast iron due to the smaller carbon content, and small intricate mild steel castings are very difficult to produce. It will be seen that in each case, the metal finishes as a product, and the shaping of the metal into the component required is an important part of engineering.

The Shaping of Metals

The shaping of metals is a fascinating part of our engineering industry, and one in which we often take little interest, as we are concerned mainly with the finished component. A bewildering variety of methods are used to produce even a simple component, but in general we can state that a metal may be shaped in three ways.

(1) Pouring liquid metal into a cavity of the shape required. (CASTING)
(2) Forcing red hot metal into the shape required. (FORGING)
(3) Shaping cold metal. (COLD-WORKING)

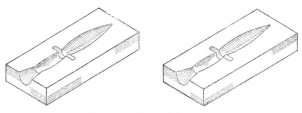

FIG. 14.—STONE MOULDS.

Casting

This is a highly skilled process, but the principles involved are very much the same as those adopted by the Romans when casting bronze short-swords. The shaping of stone, a skilled accomplishment of mankind for several thousand years, allowed the Roman craftsmen to make two halves of a mould as shown in fig. 14. It was a relatively simple matter to wedge these two half moulds together, and carefully pour molten bronze into the mould. The metal must be poured slowly and with care, to allow the escape of air and gas from the enclosed cavity within the mould. Any air trapped within the mould will form a blow hole or cavity, and will produce an unsound casting.

This is a problem which causes some headaches in the casting industry today. The moulds must be held together, as shown in fig. 15. On removal from the mould when the metal has solidified, the surplus metal at the top is broken off and the casting trimmed and polished. (Fig. 16). In this way the Romans were able to produce swords in large numbers, limited only by the amount of bronze available for casting.

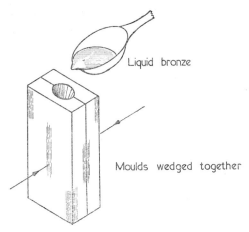

Liquid bronze

Moulds wedged together

Fig. 15.—Mould Ready for Pouring.

This part broken off

Fig. 16.—Sword Removed from Mould.

Any metal which becomes liquid when heated can be cast, and low melting point metals such as zinc or aluminium alloys are usually cast in alloy steel moulds, the process often being automatic, making the mass production of the articles possible.

High melting point metals, such as cast iron, are usually cast in sand moulds, the mould having to be destroyed in order to remove the the casting. This method is called sand casting. When steel moulds are used they are permanent, producing several hundred thousands of castings. This process is known as **die casting**. The moulds are now called dies. These alloy steel dies used in die casting are good examples of the high degree of skill possible, not only in the manufacture of the dies but also in their design, and no less important in the manufacture of the high quality crucible steel from which these dies are made.

Forging

Forging consists in forcing red hot metal into the shape required. Not all metals can be forged. Cast iron, for example, when heated red hot is even more brittle than when it is cold, and will easily break when struck with a hammer. This fault in a metal causes the metal to be known as **hot short.**

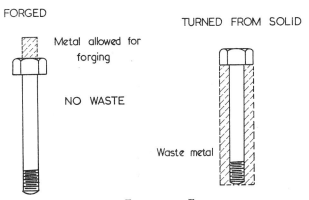

FIG. 17.—ECONOMY OF FORGING.

Mild steel, however, and many other metals, become ductile when heated to a high enough temperature, and can then be hammered or forced into the shape required. Single components would be made by a blacksmith, a highly skilled person, and with hand tools alone he is capable of producing high quality work. When large numbers of components are required, then mechanical or hydraulic methods of forcing the red hot metal into alloy steel dies are adopted, and

c

this has led to the introduction of drop forging techniques. This process is very similar to die casting.

Forging offers two distinct advantages to the engineer,

(i) greater strength

(ii) economy of material.

Fig. 17 shows a bolt made from a solid bar by machining. The shaded portion represents the metal which has been removed, and it is evident that more metal has been wasted than has been used.

Fig. 18 shows the grain flow due to the movement of the red hot metal under the forming punch. Such a bolt will possess greater strength than one machined from the solid. Perhaps fig. 19 will make this a little clearer. The grain of the wood flows around the knot and this grain flow makes the splitting of the wood a more difficult proposition.

Straight grain   Grain flow

Weak section   Strong section

FIG. 18.—STRENGTH OF FORGING.

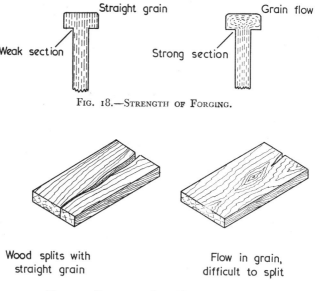

Wood splits with   Flow in grain,
straight grain   difficult to split

FIG. 19.—EFFECT OF GRAIN FLOW IN WOOD.

In this way grain flow gives added strength to the head of the bolt when it has been forged. Fig. 20 illustrates a number of components, all of which have been forged in order to give greater strength with economy of material.

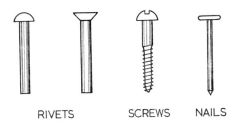

RIVETS   SCREWS   NAILS

FIG. 20.—COMPONENTS WITH FORGED HEADS.

Hot and Cold Rolling of Steel

Most of the steel produced by either the Bessemer or the open hearth furnace is poured into cast iron ingot moulds, which are lifted off when the molten steel solidifies leaving a steel ingot. These ingots are rectangular in shape and may weigh between 4 and 10 tons.

It is evident that they must be reduced into the sections required by the engineering industry. This bringing to size is done by rolling the steel between cast iron or steel rolls. Because steel becomes ductile when heated to about 1200°C, which is equivalent to white hot, the ingots are reheated to this temperature and passed through a series of rolls, which reduce the thickness, and at the same time the ingot gets longer. This process of rolling steel whilst white hot is called Hot Rolling. Fig. 21 illustrates the principle, and it is known as a **two high mill.**

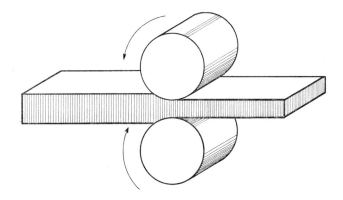

TWO HIGH MILL

FIG. 21.—PRINCIPLE OF HOT ROLLING.

Hot rolling produces good reductions, but because the metal cools rapidly during the rolling process it is imperative that the ingot be reduced as quickly as possible. Hot rolling is also used to produce a finished product known as black mild steel which is available in a wide range of sizes and sections.

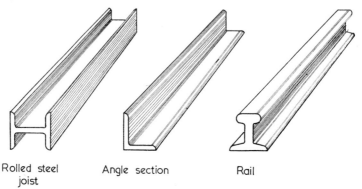

Rolled steel   Angle section   Rail
joist

FIG. 22.—HOT ROLLED STEEL SECTIONS.

Steel will rapidly oxidise or scale when in contact with the atmosphere, and this scale will be rolled into the surface of the hot rolled steel, giving it a black and scaly appearance. Thus the surface is not particularly smooth and would be most unsuitable for the manufacture of toys, car bodies, or other components that required painting or enamelling. At the same time the scale gives increased resistance to corrosion if the part is exposed to the elements.

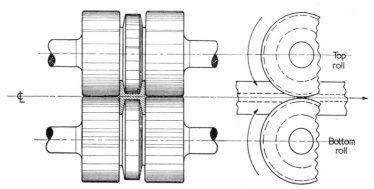

FIG. 23.—PRINCIPLE OF HOT ROLLING SECTIONS.

Steel rails, girders, ships' plates are always made from black mild or hot rolled steel because they are large in section and exposed to the weather. Fig. 22 gives some typical sections of hot rolled steel.

The production of the sections shown in fig. 22, can only be carried out if the part is symmetrical about a line parallel with the centre line of the rolls. This principle is shown in fig. 23.

In practice many passes through the rolls are required, the part being reduced by stages. A pair of rolls will be machined so that there are several stages in the rolls, unlike fig. 23 which shows a pair of rolls with a single stage. Fig. 24 gives the approximate stages required to form a rectangular bar or billet into an H section rolled steel joist.

FIG. 24.—STAGES OR PASSES TO FORM H SECTION

Cold Rolling of Steel

Many mild steel components require a bright smooth surface and this is achieved by cold rolling the steel into the sizes and thicknesses of metal required. The steel is first hot rolled near the finished size, and then pickled in acid to remove the scale.

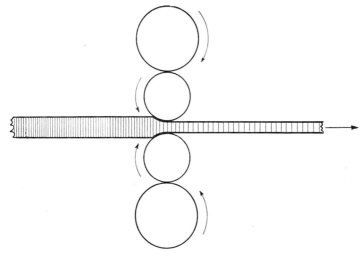

FOUR HIGH MILL

FIG. 25.—PRINCIPLE OF COLD ROLLING

It is then passed through a four high mill, which provides the additional pressures required to roll the cold steel. Fig. 25 illustrates the principle. The surfaces of the rolls are highly polished and they burnish the steel sheet giving it a high polish. At the same time the steel will "work harden" due to the pressures exerted on the steel sheet as it passes through the rolls, and this gives the steel a degree of hardness or spring.

Reductions in size as a result of cold rolling are small, because not only does the metal possess its original strength, but the stresses also set up in resisting the pressure of the rolls tend to increase the strength of the metal, and give it a distinct internal grain effect along the direction of rolling. Great care must be exercised when bending cold rolled steel, or bright mild steel as it is commonly called. Fig. 26 shows what will happen if bright mild steel is bent with the grain. This grain is not visible on the outside of the metal but is present within the structure. Faint lines indicating the direction of rolling can usually be detected on the bright mild sheet or strip. Reference back to fig. 18 and then to fig. 19, will show how this grain is put to good effect when a part is forged. A suitable heat treatment process will remove this grain effect in bright mild steel.

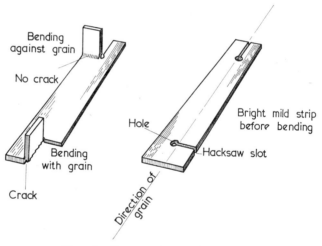

FIG. 26.—GRAIN IN BRIGHT MILD STEEL.

Bright mild steel, however, still has many advantages. Its dimensional accuracy is far better than black mild. The corners will be sharp, and the surface suitable for receiving scriber lines when marking out. It is, however, more expensive than black mild, and will rust immediately it is exposed to the atmosphere.

Fig. 27 shows the comparison between bright and black mild steel bar.

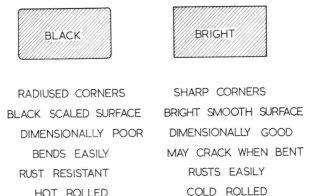

RADIUSED CORNERS	SHARP CORNERS
BLACK SCALED SURFACE	BRIGHT SMOOTH SURFACE
DIMENSIONALLY POOR	DIMENSIONALLY GOOD
BENDS EASILY	MAY CRACK WHEN BENT
RUST RESISTANT	RUSTS EASILY
HOT ROLLED	COLD ROLLED

FIG. 27.—CHARACTERISTICS OF BLACK AND BRIGHT MILD STEEL.

Summary

Three engineering components can now be chosen to illustrate how engineers use metals to the best possible advantage.

Fig. 28 shows a simple grey cast iron surface plate. It must not receive any rough usage and is subject only to compressive forces. It needs a smooth, even wearing surface so that a scribing block will slide easily when marking out. A large mass of metal is needed if the surface is to be flat. Grey cast iron is ideally suited for this job. It is cheap, easily cast, and will have graphite in the structure, which will act as a lubricant. Thus a great number of surface plates are made from grey cast iron.

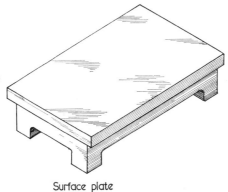

Surface plate

FIG. 28.—COMPONENT CAST IN GREY CAST IRON.

Fig. 29 shows a crank shaft for a car engine. This component is subject to severe stresses and must be as strong as possible. For this reason it will be forged, the grain flow around the journals and main bearings giving great strength. A medium carbon steel crank shaft would be cheap yet serviceable.

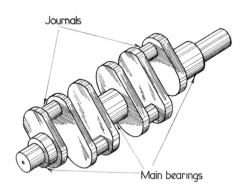

CRANKSHAFT

FIG. 29.—COMPONENT FORGED IN MEDIUM CARBON STEEL.

Fig. 30 shows the side piece of a bicycle pedal. Bright mild steel would be used, the part being produced on press tools. The smooth bright surface would allow chromium plating which would prevent rusting. The additional strength produced by cold rolling would be an advantage.

The punches and dies used to produce this component, see fig. 2, are good examples of the use of a crucible steel.

Pedal side piece

FIG. 30.—COMPONENT PRODUCED FROM BRIGHT MILD STEEL.

QUESTIONS ON CHAPTER ONE
The questions in Part A can be answered by reference to this chapter Part B contains more difficult questions and will require reference to a more comprehensive text book. Suitable books are readily available in the college or public library.

Part A

1. Explain what is meant by the term pig iron. Why is this metal never used for engineering components?

2. Show by means of a neat diagram, how the iron and slag are removed from a blast furnace.

3. What is the purpose of adding limestone to the charge in a blast furnace?

4. Make a neat sketch of an engineering component you would make from grey cast iron. What manufacturing process would you adopt to produce this component? Give three reasons.

5. What is the essential difference between cast iron and steel? Give one reason why steel is stronger.

6. What is the essential difference between steel and wrought iron? How is wrought iron produced? Why is it expensive?

7. State the two main steel-making processes. Which method is in greater use? Give two reasons.

8. Why is it necessary to make high quality steel by the crucible process?

9. What principle is adopted on the open hearth furnace to reach the high temperatures required for steel making? Illustrate your answer by means of a suitable sketch.

10. State two advantages to be gained by forging a steel component. Can all metals be forged?

11. What are the characteristics of:
    (1) Bright mild steel.
    (2) Black mild steel.
    Tabulate your answer.

Part B

1. Reference to fig. 4, shows that a great amount of heat is lost from the open top of the blast furnace. Make a neat sketch of a device that would enable the furnace to be charged with no loss of heat.

2. Fig. 2 shows the punches and die used in a press tool. What steel would be used for these punches and die? Give three alloying elements.

3. Make a neat sketch showing the principle involved when extruding metal.

4. What is meant by the term "work hardening"? Give two effects on the physical properties of mild steel when it has been work hardened.

2 Heat Treatment of Steel

WE have seen in Chapter 1 that when steel is heated white hot it can be rolled with comparative ease. This is due to the fact that the physical properties of the steel undergo a change caused by the rise in the temperature. It is more ductile than when it is cold, and can be rolled or forged into the desired shape or section.

It can be said, then, that all heat treatment of steel will involve a rise in temperature, or heating of the steel, and fig. 31 is a simple line diagram showing some of the basic heat treatments and the approximate temperatures at which they are carried out. Note also the cooling rates. The vertical line represents temperature in degrees centigrade, rising to a maximum of 1200°C. To the left of this line, and corresponding with the heat treatment process, is given the colour of the steel when heated to the temperature indicated. This simple diagram would be quite suitable for workshop applications of the heat treatment of steel, but the success of the operation would depend to a large extent on the skill and experience of the operator. For production work and components of good quality, it is essential that the process be carried out in furnaces of the correct type, fitted with accurate pyrometers indicating the temperature within the furnace. There is, however, a great deal of satisfaction to be gained by hardening and tempering a small cutting tool correctly, using simple workshop methods.

Hardening High Carbon Steel

High carbon steels contain between 0.8% and 1.3% carbon. These steels have excellent hardening qualities, and a popular choice is 1.0% carbon, of which silver steel is a good example.

Because of the smaller carbon content, steels below 0.8% carbon do not harden so appreciably as those in excess of 0.8% carbon; thus a mild steel of 0.3% carbon would gain little or no hardness when heated and quenched. Perhaps the hardening and tempering of a cold chisel will serve to illustrate the principles and processes of hardening. Octagonal cast steel bar will be chosen having a carbon content of about 0.9%. The end has been forged and filed to shape and some care has been exercised in giving the working end of the chisel a good smooth

26

finish. This will allow easy polishing of the end after it has been hardened. Reference to the diagram (fig. 31) shows that the chisel must be heated to cherry red, approximately 820°C, and at this temperature it must be plunged into cold clean water. Thus the hardening process for high carbon steel is relatively simple: heat to cherry red and quench in cold water.

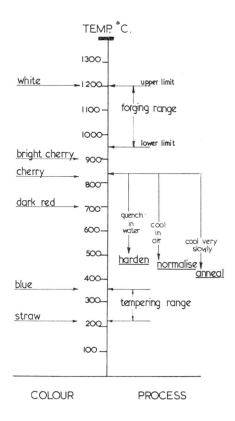

FIG. 31.—PRACTICAL HEAT TREATMENT OF STEEL.

There is one important rule to be observed when hardening a tool, namely harden only the working part of the tool. This is illustrated in fig. 32, and it will be seen that only about ⅜ in. of the chisel edge will be heated to cherry and then quenched. The heating of this edge will call for skill in the manipulation of the blow-pipe. If the flame is directed onto the tip, then overheating is almost certain to occur due to the small mass of metal at the point. It is vital that the edge be cherry red and not taken above this temperature or the overheated part will be likely to fracture when the chisel is put into use.

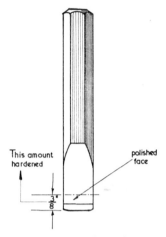

This amount hardened

polished face

$\frac{3}{8}$

FIG. 32.—FLAT COLD CHISEL.

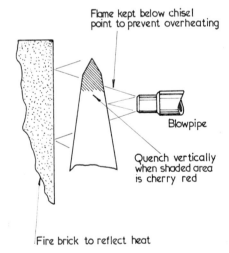

Flame kept below chisel point to prevent overheating

Blowpipe

Quench vertically when shaded area is cherry red

Fire brick to reflect heat

FIG. 33.—METHOD OF HEATING A COLD CHISEL

Fig. 33 shows the technique to be adopted. Keep the flame below the point and quench when the first $\frac{1}{2}$ inch is uniformly cherry red. Ensure that the chisel is kept in a vertical position when quenched and move it around in the water. On removal from the water the chisel point will now be dead hard and too hard to file. It is, in fact, harder than a file, and will, quite easily, leave a mark along the teeth of the file. It is also exceedingly brittle due to its extreme hardness. It is evident, then, that a further process must be carried out in order to remove some of the brittleness and thus toughen the chisel point so that it will stand up to the impact imparted by the hammer blow. This process is called 'Tempering'.

Tempering High Carbon Steel

The object of tempering a high carbon tool is to toughen the cutting edge and thus make it more suitable for the sort of work it has to do. A chisel edge which has not received sufficient temper may be too hard and too brittle. In this condition it is dangerous; a small portion may well fly off when the chisel is in use, and such a fragment entering the operator's eye could cause serious injury. Tempering then, is a vital operation and calls for great care. We see from fig. 31, that the tempering range is quite small, starting at approximately 230°C and finishing at 320°C.

At these temperatures the steel will not even be dull red, but if the steel is polished prior to heating, then oxide films will form on the heated surface. The colour of these oxide films will depend on the temperature of the steel, and will, therefore, give an indication of the temperature.

In this way the oxidisation of heated steel is put to good advantage by the practical engineer. Table 1 shows the connection between:

(i) temperature,

(ii) colour of oxide film,

(iii) conditions the tool will stand,

(iv) typical tools used in engineering.

It will be noted that the tool gets tougher as the tempering temperature increases, losing hardness in the process, and for this reason care must be exercised when sharpening high carbon steel tools at the grindstone. Due to the friction between the emery wheel and the tool, heat is rapidly generated and this heat must cause a rise in temperature which will, in effect, soften the tool.

Reference to Table 1, shows that the chisel is a tool which must stand up to heavy blows, and this means it must be tempered to approximately 260°C. This temperature is equivalent to a dark brown oxide film.

TABLE I

CONNECTION BETWEEN TEMPERATURE, COLOUR,
PHYSICAL PROPERTIES OF HIGH CARBON STEEL

Temp. ° C.	Colour of Oxide film	Conditions	Typical Tools	
230	Light straw	Some pressure but no blows	Scribers, scrapers	Hard
240	Dark straw	Heavy pressure light blows	Turning tools, drills	
250	Light brown	Medium blows and torques	Centre punches, taps, reamers	
260	Dark brown	Heavy blows and torques	Drills, chisels, heavy punches, large taps	
280	Purple	Very heavy blows	Hammer heads, axes	
320	Blue	Shock loading	Springs	Tough

Method of Tempering

The first rule of tempering is to take plenty of time over this important operation. To apply the heat directly on the cutting edge is bad practice. If this is done then the outside surface of the steel will rapidly rise in temperature and oxide films will form, but the internal metal will still be well below the temperature indicated by the oxide film on the external surface. Such a cutting edge would be brittle and liable to fracture.

Fig. 34 illustrates the correct technique. Keep the flame well below the cutting edge. In this way, the heat will travel up the chisel by conduction and the oxide films will be a true representation of the temperature of the whole mass of the chisel edge. The colours will move up as shown in fig. 34, and when the cutting edge turns a dark brown, the chisel can be quenched in water. This method offers many advantages. It will be seen that the temper of the chisel runs from hard at the chisel edge to tough where the oxide film is blue. Below the blue colour the chisel will have its normal condition.

It is possible to harden and temper a chisel in one heating, but the method described above will give better control over the tempering process. For best results a good polish must be put on the chisel edge after hardening, care being taken not to handle the chisel edge after such polishing. The presence of oil or grease on the polished surface will affect the colour of the oxide films.

The longer the heating, the slower will be the movement of the oxide films and they will be further apart. This will allow better control over the tempering process.

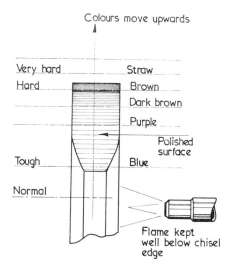

FIG. 34.—TEMPERING A COLD CHISEL.

Testing a cold chisel

It is essential to test any tool which has been hardened and tempered by the method described above. The test should be a severe one, and if successful, then the chisel can be used with confidence.

Fig. 35 illustrates a suitable test for the chisel in question. It will be noted that the chisel is in point contact with the work and this will be a severe test for the chisel edge when the chisel is subjected to a heavy hammer blow. Fig. 35 shows also the possible effects on the chisel edge of such a test. A well hardened and tempered chisel will suffer no damage, except for a burnishing of the edge where it has made contact with the test piece. Eye protection, such as goggles, should be worn when carrying out such a test.

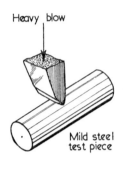

Too soft   Too hard   Tool correct

FIG. 35.—TESTING A COLD CHISEL.

Normalising

This is another process shown on fig. 31. Once again the steel is heated to cherry red and allowed to cool in still air. This means that it is allowed to cool in some secluded corner of the workshop. This process is called **"normalising"**.

The object of normalising, as the name suggests, is to restore to the steel its normal properties. We have seen in Chapter 1, that the cold rolling of steel gives to the metal a grain effect along the direction of rolling, and the steel gets harder and stronger. The physical properties of the steel are changed by the cold rolling process; normalising bright mild steel will remove any of these changes.

In general we may state that normalising is carried out for **two** main reasons:

    (i) to remove the stresses set up by cold working,
    (ii) to remove the grain effect brought about by cold rolling.

Two examples will serve to illustrate the workshop applications of normalising. Fig. 36 shows a bar of $1\frac{1}{2}'' \times 1\frac{1}{2}''$ bright mild steel, which is to be machined as shown, for use as the body of a small toolmaker's vice. It is possible that the bar has been ground square all over prior to marking out, and if this has been done then it may be considered as wasted effort.

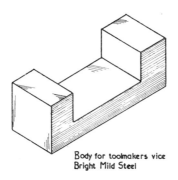

Body for toolmakers vice
Bright Mild Steel

FIG. 36.—COMPONENT REQUIRING NORMALISING.

The removal of the centre portion will cause a re-distribution of stresses which will cause severe distortion of the bar, necessitating complete re-grinding of the component. The causes for such distortion are shown in fig. 37, where it can be seen that the removal of metal has set up unequal forces.

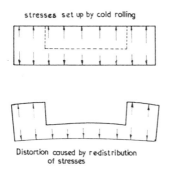

stresses set up by cold rolling

Distortion caused by redistribution of stresses

FIG. 37.—CAUSE OF DISTORTION IN MACHINED BRIGHT MILD STEEL.

If, therefore, accurate work is to be carried out on bright mild steel stock, it is essential that the bar be first normalised. The process is simple. Heat to cherry red and allow to cool by putting it in some con-

D

venient place. It is wise to chalk the word 'HOT' on it and thus possibly save someone a nasty burn.

We are already familiar with the second example which is shown in fig. 38. In this case we wish to bend a component along the grain, and to do so in the cold rolled state will almost certainly cause the metal to crack along the bend. Once again the steel would be normalised, after which it can be bent with every confidence.

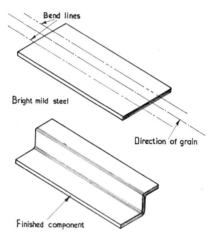

FIG. 38.—NORMALISING TO PREVENT CRACKING.

The great objection to normalising is that the metal will scale when heated to cherry red. This is certain to occur if the part is heated with a blow-lamp, especially if too much air is allowed to mix with the gas. There are, however, several types of furnaces, such as muffle and atmosphere controlled types where scaling can be kept to a minimum.

Annealing

It will seen from fig. 31 that the only difference between annealing and normalising is in the rate of cooling. To anneal we heat to cherry red and allow to cool as slowly as possible. If the part is heated in a furnace, then the best method is to turn the furnace off and allow the part to cool with the furnace. If the part is heated with a blow-lamp, then it will be necessary to bury it in hot ashes or sand.

The object of annealing is to make the steel as ductile, or as soft as possible, so that it can be easily bent or machined. It is usual to supply all cast and tool steels in the annealed condition so that they are readily machined.

Fig. 39 illustrates a bracket made from bright mild steel. Because of the severity of the bends it would be annealed before bending, thus giving the steel maximum ductility. The steel will, of course, scale as in normalising, and manufacturers who require sheet steel which has to be severely cold worked, for example car bodies, receive it in a condition known as *cold rolled close annealed*. This means that the steel has been annealed in a closed atmosphere. In effect no oxygen is allowed to get at the surface of the steel at the annealing temperature. In the result there is no scaling of steel sheets annealed in this manner.

Made from $\frac{1}{8}$" x 1"
Bright mild steel

FIG. 39.—MILD STEEL BRACKET REQUIRING ANNEALING.

Case-Hardening

It has already been stated that mild steel cannot be hardened by heating to cherry red and quenching in water. This is due to its low carbon content of approximately 0.25%. It is, however, possible to increase the carbon content of the outer surface of a mild steel component by heating the component to cherry red, and immersing it in a substance rich in carbon. The amount of carbon absorbed and the depth of penetration will depend chiefly on the time the heated steel is in contact with the carbonaceous material. There are several methods in use and the addition of carbon can be achieved by using charcoal, liquid salts or even gases. Whichever medium is used the principle remains the same—the addition of carbon to the outside surface of a mild steel component and then quenching the component whilst cherry red into water.

Because the outside surface of the steel possesses a high carbon content, it will become hard, whilst the inner part or the core will still have a low carbon content and will not harden. This process is known as **case-hardening.**

A mild steel component treated in this way will have many advantages. The outside surface will be hard and able to stand up to wear and abrasion; the remainder of the component will be tough, possessing the properties of mild steel. Further, the component will cost much less than one made from high carbon steel. If high carbon steel were used and hardened, then it would not stand up to a sudden blow or shock, as the component would be hard through its whole section and thus brittle.

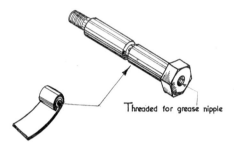

Threaded for grease nipple

FIG. 40.—CASE-HARDENED MILD STEEL SHACKLE BOLT.

Fig. 40 illustrates the application of a typical case-hardened component. It is a shackle bolt for pivoting the rear springs of a motor car to the chassis. This bolt will be subject to wear occasioned by the flexing of the spring as it takes the weight of the car and meets undulations on the road surface. At the same time if the car passes over pot-holes or other rough surfaces, the bolt is likely to receive severe blows or shocks. Ideally we would require a tough bolt with a hard outside surface, and due to the large number of cars produced a cheap material would be essential. Case-hardened mild steel will certainly be used, a further advantage being that the hexagonal head can be forged, thus giving the important economy of material mentioned in Chapter 1.

It is possible to case-harden such a component at the forge. The bolt would be turned from mild steel, heated to cherry red, and then dipped into case-hardening powder. It is then reheated and the powder which has adhered to the surface will be absorbed by the heated steel. It is wise to repeat the process, making sure that adequate powder has been absorbed, but care should be taken not to overheat the steel. Keep the temperature bright cherry red and after two immersions in the powder, quench in cold water.

This method would not, of course, be used when the shackle bolts are mass produced, and care would be taken to ensure that the threaded portion was not hardened.

Simple Forging

Reference to fig. 31 will show that the forging range falls between 1200°C and 950°C. There is little doubt that hand forging calls for a remarkably high degree of skill, knowledge and judgement. Unless a student is apprenticed to a skilled blacksmith he is not likely to achieve much forging ability. It will be sufficient then, for the purposes of this chapter, if we illustrate some of the main basic forging techniques. The blacksmith, like any other practical engineer, is concerned with producing a given component, and the processes he uses are all calculated to bring about the desired shape of the component with the minimum effort and time.

Upsetting

The head of the shackle bolt shown in fig. 40, would be produced by the process known as "upsetting".

This principle is shown in fig. 41, and is widely used for the production of rivets, bolts, screws, and many other components, added strength being obtained by the grain flow of the metal. It is, of course, possible to upset a bar in any position, by heating only the portion to be upset.

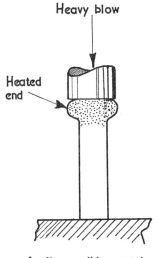

Heavy blow

Heated end

Anvil or solid support

FIG. 41.—UPSETTING.

Drawing Down

This process consists of lengthening or elongating the metal and calls for considerable skill. Several methods are possible and fig. 42 illustrates the principle and the methods that can be used.

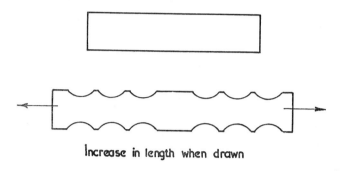

Increase in length when drawn

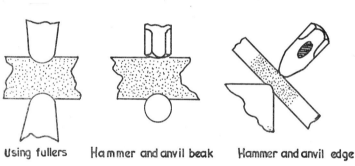

Using fullers   Hammer and anvil beak   Hammer and anvil edge

FIG. 42.—PRINCIPLES AND METHODS OF DRAWING DOWN.

Setting Down

This operation usually follows drawing down, and can be accomplished with a hammer or with a hammer and flatter. This method would be used for finishing off square or rectangular work. Fig. 43 illustrates the principle.

Swaging

Round work is produced with the aid of swages. These swages are in sets of two, a top and bottom swage. The bottom swage fits into the anvil, whilst the blacksmith manipulates the top swage whilst it is struck by his assistant or striker. The principle is shown in fig. 44.

It may now be appreciated that the processes described require the skill of two operators. It is the blacksmith who wields the tools and shapes the metal, whilst his striker gives the necessary force by wielding a hammer or sledge. Both are highly skilled and work together as a team, and it is not likely that the engineering apprentice will attain the skill and experience required.

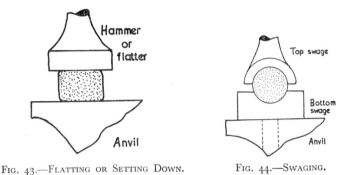

FIG. 43.—FLATTING OR SETTING DOWN.   FIG. 44.—SWAGING.

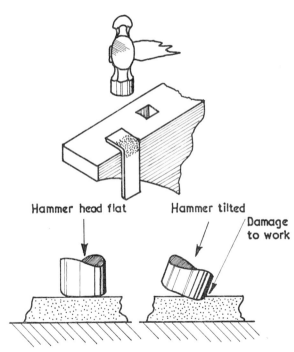

FIG. 45.—BENDING ON THE ANVIL WITH THE HAMMER.

Bending

This is an operation which may well be carried out by the engineering apprentice. There are a few simple rules to be observed, depending upon the type of bend required.

Right-angle bends

For work of thin section, the edge of the anvil can be used. Care should be taken to ensure that the hammer head makes flat contact with the heated steel, or deep impressions will be left on the steel. If the part is to be hardened, these impressions may lead to cracking of the component as they cause a source of weakness from which a crack could start. Fig. 45 will make this point clear.

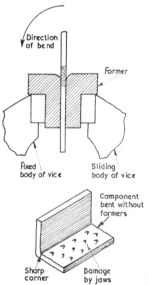

FIG. 46.—BENDING IN THE VICE.

Bending at the vice can be used for thicker sections, but it is bad practice if formers are not used. The jaws of a vice are hardened steel and they are usually serrated to increase the gripping action. Such jaws will severely damage the job, and the very sharp bend produced would be undesirable. It is better to use a pair of mild steel formers having the required radius filed on them. The bend should be hammered away from the operator, the fixed member of the vice taking the forces of the hammer blow (fig. 46). The bending of radiused work may also be carried out in the vice using round bars as formers, care being taken once again to avoid damage to the work. A useful aid is to have a special former with a V groove, and this will hold the round bar in a truly horizontal plane, allowing speedy bending of the work, essential because the work is continually losing heat. This method is shown in fig. 47.

Summary

The advantages of the heat treatment of carbon steel can now be illustrated by reference to fig. 48.

Let us assume that we wish to change the shape of a hand file and also to drill and tap a hole to take an additional handle. In order to drill and tap this hole, the file should be as soft or as machinable as possible.

Therefore, we would anneal the file by heating it to cherry red and allowing it to cool as slowly as possible. After drilling and tapping the hole, the part to be bent would be heated to bright cherry and bent as shown. It is now necessary to harden the file, and this would mean re-heating to cherry red and quenching vertically in cold water. Under no circumstances would the tang be hardened but only the working portion of the file.

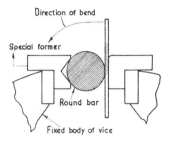

FIG. 47.—BENDING LARGE RADII IN THE VICE.

Tempering would be carried out by polishing one edge, and placing the file on a steel plate resting on firebricks. The heat from a blow-pipe would be directed below the plate and the file quenched when the

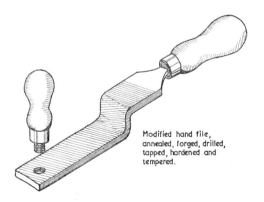

FIG. 48.—PRACTICAL WORKSHOP HEAT TREATMENT.

colour approaches dark straw. Because of our knowledge of heat treatment we are able to modify this file to the shape required, and still produce an efficient cutting tool, having the correct hardness and temper.

QUESTIONS ON CHAPTER TWO

Part A

1. Make a neat sketch of a high carbon steel cutting tool used at the bench for removing metal. Indicate clearly the hardened portion.

2. Write down the name of a hand-tool you would temper to the following colours:
   (i)   dark straw
   (ii) purple
   (iii) blue
   (iv) brown.

3. Describe with the aid of neat diagrams how you would harden and temper a scriber point.

4. Make a neat sketch of a component you would case-harden, giving **three** reasons for your choice.

5. What is meant by the term 'normalising'? Describe briefly this heat treatment process.

6. Make a neat sketch of a component you would normalise, giving a reason.

7. What is the essential difference between normalising and annealing?

8. Make a neat sketch of a component you would anneal, giving a reason for this heat treatment process.

9. Illustrate with a neat diagram the following forging processes:
    (i)   upsetting
    (ii) flatting
    (iii) bending
    (iv) drawing down.

10. Why is it essential to proceed as quickly as possible with a forging operation?

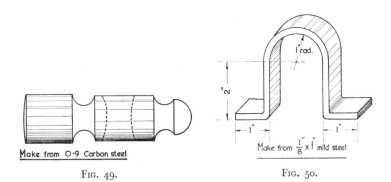

Make from 0·9 Carbon steel

Fig. 49.

Make from $\frac{1}{8}'' \times 1''$ mild steel

Fig. 50.

Part B

1. The hammer head shown in fig. 49 is made from 0.9% carbon steel, and is to be hardened and tempered. Describe in some detail how you would carry out these processes.

2. What is meant by 'hot plate' tempering? Sketch a suitable component you would temper by this method.

3. What are the advantages of a **muffle** furnace for heat treating a steel component?

4. Describe how you would bend the component shown in fig. 50. Calculate the overall length of the component before bending.

3 The Joining of Metals

ENGINEERS are concerned with making components, and usually the finished product will consist of a large number of components joined together in one way or another. Motor cars, bicycles and washing

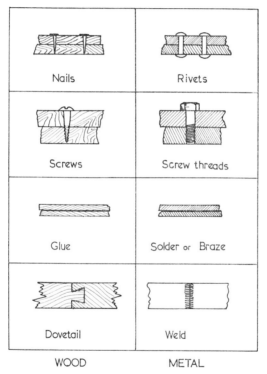

WOOD	METAL
Nails	Rivets
Screws	Screw threads
Glue	Solder or Braze
Dovetail	Weld

FIG. 51.—PRINCIPLES OF WOOD AND METAL JOINING.

machines are all examples of finished products made up of a large number of separate parts. It is true to say that engineers are mainly concerned with metals, but it must be remembered that wood was once widely used as an engineering material. Wooden gears were used in windmills and even the first machine tools were constructed from wood.

The principles involved in the joining of separate parts have changed little over the centuries, and it is the introduction of new materials that demand a change in techniques or processes. That the principles remain somewhat similar is shown in fig. 51, where the joining of wood is compared with the joining of metal. It is, of course, much easier to work wood than it is to work metal, and for this reason wood is still in wide demand for a large number of articles.

With the aid of fig. 51, we may now examine the principles and techniques involved in the joining of metals. Generally speaking the type of joint used will depend primarily on whether it is to be permanent or temporary, and, secondly, on the sort of work the joint will have to withstand.

Riveting

This process can be considered as a permanent method of joining metals together, and is equivalent to nailing in woodwork. It is generally used for relatively thin work, such as the steel sheets making up the hulls of ships or the aluminium alloy sheets used for aircraft fuselages.

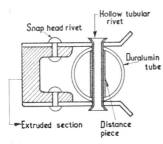

FIG. 52.—RIVETED AIRCRAFT ASSEMBLY.

Whilst wood will hold a nail by frictional forces, this is not possible when working with metal, therefore rivets will have heads cold or hot worked equivalent to the head on the opposite side. Many types of rivets are available in many different metals, and a rivet is classified by the shape of the head, its diameter and length. Considerable skill is required if efficient riveting is to be carried out. Fig. 52 illustrates some applications of riveting in the aircraft industry.

For this kind of work it is essential that the heads of the rivets be polished prior to riveting, as the presence of file marks may lead to cracking when the head is brought to shape.

In the example shown in fig. 52 all the materials are aluminium alloys giving good strength for light weight, very necessary in the aircraft industry. When two parts require to be held together with great force, as in the riveting of ship or boiler plates, the rivets are heated red hot and riveted in this condition. On cooling the rivet tends to contract and very great forces are involved, pulling the plates very tightly together. Large diameter rivets are also easier to work when they are red hot.

Screw Fastening Devices

Screw fastening devices are invariably used to join metal parts together which may have to be taken apart at a later date for purposes of repair or replacement. They make, in effect, a temporary joint. Many types of screw fastening devices are used in engineering.

There are a few simple rules governing the correct choice of a screw fastening device, and we will consider firstly the nut and bolt.

Nuts and Bolts

In general it can be stated that a nut and bolt will be used when both sides of the parts to be joined are readily accessible. This will allow the use of a spanner to tighten the nut and possibly the use of a spanner to prevent turning of the bolt. The use of nuts and bolts also offers saving in the manufacture of the components, as only clearance holes require to be drilled and no threads are required in the components. Therefore, in the event of damaged or stripped threads, it is a cheap and simple matter to replace a bolt or nut, whilst a stripped thread in a component may involve scrapping the component.

Fig. 53 illustrates a typical use for a nut and bolt; note that the bolt is only threaded for part of its length. Nuts and bolts subject to vibration will require a device to prevent the nut working loose, and this is especially necessary when the parts joined form a vital assembly as in the steering mechanism of a motor car.

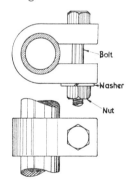
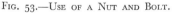
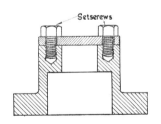

FIG. 53.—USE OF A NUT AND BOLT.   FIG. 54.—USE OF SET SCREWS.

Most bolts used in engineering have hexagonal heads and nuts, but square headed bolts may also be used.

Set Screws

Unlike a bolt, a set screw will be threaded for most of its length, and it is generally used where a nut and bolt is impracticable or impossible.

There are many instances in an engineering assembly where set screws must be used for the reason given above, and this means that the component must be threaded to receive the set screw. In the event of excessive tightening there is a real danger of stripping the thread in the part being joined, therefore great care must be exercised when tightening set screws. Fig. 54 illustrates a typical use for a set screw. Hexagonal head set screws are widely used, but set screws may have countersunk heads which will require the use of a screw driver for tightening purposes. It is difficult to tighten a set screw efficiently with a screw driver and, for this reason, socket screws have been introduced having an hexagonal form within the head of the screw. Tightening is carried out with an hexagonal key which is a much more positive method than the blade of a screw driver. Socket screws are widely used in the manufacture of machine tools, press tools, jigs and fixtures. Fig. 55 illustrates a typical use of a socket screw.

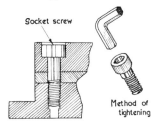
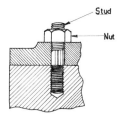

FIG. 55.—USE OF SOCKET SCREWS.   FIG. 56.—USE OF A STUD.

Studs

Because of the positive fit of the hexagonal key into the socket screw, considerable tightening pressure can be exerted. Where heavy pressures are required to ensure gas-tight or water-tight joints, then it is customary to use studs. The studs are first screwed home into the component and the tightening effected by mild steel nuts. Any damage caused by excessive tightening will be to either the nut or the stud, and these are easily replaced. Studs are very necessary for joining parts to grey cast iron components because the tensile strength of grey cast iron is low, and excessive tightening into a grey cast iron thread may cause crumbling or stripping of the thread and possibly make the casting unserviceable.

Fig. 56 illustrates the use of studs for holding down a cylinder head on the cylinder block of a motor car engine. The joining of the cylinder head to the cylinder block must be a temporary joint because it will be necessary, at a later date, to remove the head to recondition the engine, yet the joint must be both gas and water-tight and stand up to the forces caused by the expansion of the petrol-air mixture. Mild steel studs are ideal for this purpose.

Location of Engineering Components

It is seldom that nuts and bolts or set screws are used to position or locate components accurately. The main purpose of a threaded fastener is to hold the parts together and it is customary to drill clearance holes for bolts and studs. When accurate alignment is required the following methods may be used.

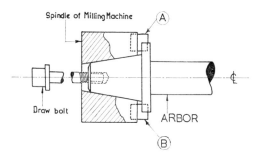

FIG. 57.—LOCATION OF A MILLING MACHINE ARBOR.

Tapers

Tapers are widely used for the location of one part accurately to another. There is also the additional advantage that the tightening force will tend to increase the mating of one part to the other and thus increase the accuracy of location. This principle is illustrated in fig. 57, which shows the method of joining the arbor of a milling machine to the spindle. It is essential that the centre-line of the arbor be a continuation of the centre-line of the spindle if the arbor is to run true, and tapers are accurately ground on both parts to provide precise alignment. A draw bolt is used to pull the arbor tightly into the taper in the spindle.

Note that the torque is transmitted by the parts A and B.

Registers

These are often used for accurate alignment when two cylindrical parts are joined together. Fig. 58 shows two cylindrical components turned on a lathe. Accurate alignment of their bores is achieved by machining a recess in Part A, into which the register or turned portion on Part B is a good fit. The parts may be held together by nuts and bolts.

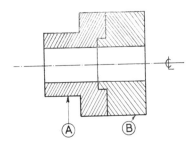

FIG. 58.—ALIGNING CYLINDRICAL COMPONENTS
WITH A REGISTER.

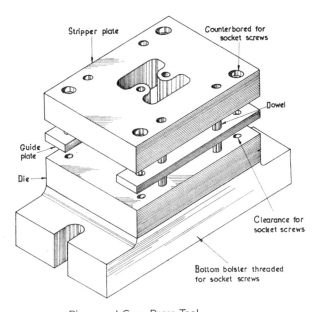

Pierce and Crop Press Tool

FIG. 59.—THE JOINING AND ALIGNING OF THE COMPONENT PARTS OF A
PRESS TOOL.

Dowels

The use of dowels is usually confined to the accurate alignment of
plane surfaces or flat components, and ensures that the parts will re-
assemble accurately after removal. This is very necessary in most press
tool work, and fig. 59 shows a typical Pierce and Crop tool having four
dowels. In this assembly, the stripper plate, guide plates, die and bottom

bolster must re-assemble accurately on each occasion the die is removed for re-grinding. Note the use of socket screws for holding the parts together with clearance holes in stripper, guide plates and die. It is evident that the joining of these components calls for a high degree of skill, involving the use of expensive machine tools.

There are, however, other methods of joining metals involving the minimum equipment, and providing rapid joining of two parts.

Soldering

The principle of soldering is similar to that of gluing two pieces of wood together, as shown in fig. 51. This means that a liquid film of metal is interposed between the two surfaces to be joined, giving, on solidification, a jointing compound between the metals. Soldering is divided into two types, soft soldering, and hard soldering, and the type of soldering used will depend mainly on the strength required from the finished joint.

Soft Soldering

This method is generally used for joints having a small surface area, and not likely to be subjected to undue forces. The strength of a soldered joint is not high as the solder used is an alloy of lead and tin, both low strength metals, but chosen for their low melting points. It is a general principle, then, that every effort is made to strengthen the joint by careful design, and not to rely on the actual solder contact. The strength of the joint is greatly increased by the devices used and the presence of the solder tends to make the joint permanent, and will ensure that the joint is water-tight and gas-tight, where applicable.

In the electrical industry a great number of joints are made, especially so in the manufacture of radio and television receivers. The joining of a copper wire to a brass clip is a very common example, and soft soldering provides the cheapest and most rapid method of joining. In order to observe our first rule, which is to increase the strength of the joint, it is a wise plan to take a loop of the wire through the hole in the brass clip. The application of solder will now make this a sound joint, the loop providing the strength and the solder giving good electrical contact, and also permanency to the joint. Fig. 60 illustrates the method.

The soldering of tinned steel containers has been carried on for many years, and is a good example of the use of soft solder to produce an airtight or water-tight joint. Once again the strength of the joint is obtained by lapping the ends of the can into one another, very similar to the looping of the copper into the hole in the brass clip. A very strong joint is produced in this way, a fact appreciated by the

E

Romans, who made their lead pipes by a similar method. The principle is shown in fig. 61; note that some of the solder is drawn into the joint by capillary action.

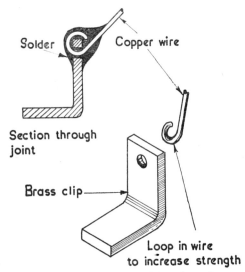

FIG. 60.—SOFT SOLDERING WIRE TO A CLIP.

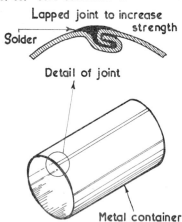

FIG. 61.—SOFT SOLDERING A METAL CONTAINER.

Most of us are familiar with the serious results that may occur when a soldered nipple on the end of a bicycle brake cable breaks away from the cable. Provided we remember that the strength of the joint is not dependent on the solder, it is not difficult to carry out a suitable repair.

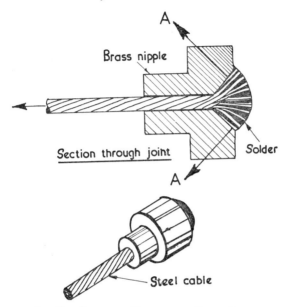

A

Brass nipple

Section through joint

Solder

A

FIG. 62.—JOINING A NIPPLE TO A STEEL CABLE.

Steel cable

Fig. 62 shows the principle involved. It will be seen that the end of the brass nipple is countersunk, and the strands of the cable are splayed out in a uniform manner within this countersink. If, now, we fill the gaps between these strands with molten solder, on solidification a solid wedge of steel and solder will be formed, and the forces set up by application of the brake will now act in the direction of the arrows A, and will tend to burst the brass nipple. This is a good example of how engineers improve the strength of a soldered joint. A joint made by just soldering the cable into the bore of the nipple would be most dangerous.

Principles of Soldering

For small areas of contact a soldering poker is invariably used. The bit, or working end, is made of copper because of its ability to conduct heat onto the metal of the job. The bit may be heated externally in a gas flame or coke fire, or can be electrically heated if the bit is used for very small work.

The principles of soldering are important and successful work can only be achieved by strict adherence to the principles outlined below.

Fig. 63 illustrates the soldering action achieved with the use of a poker, and the diagram magnifies the end of the copper bit. We have, in effect, stopped the poker during its movement along the joint and are now able to examine, in detail, the actual soldering action. Note, firstly, the direction taken by the poker as shown in arrow A. This is important because one purpose of the bit is to transfer heat to the work prior to the adherence of the solder. This is achieved by inclining the poker as shown. The amount of heat present in the poker will depend mainly on the mass or size of the bit, and large pokers are preferred because they enable a greater amount of soldering between re-heats. For this reason the small pokers used in electrical work are internally heated by means of a heating element, otherwise more time would be spent heating the poker than would be spent in actual soldering. Note that the bit also acts as a reservoir for the solder and for this reason a bit must be "tinned" before use. This means that the bit is heated (not red hot) lightly, filed to remove the oxide film, dipped in flux and then inserted in some liquid solder. When the solder "takes" to the bit it has a silvery appearance, hence the name "tinning". A well tinned bit is capable of picking up solder from a clean piece of wood.

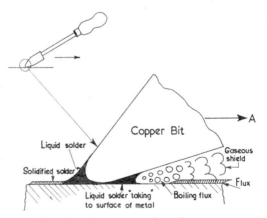

FIG. 63.—PRINCIPLE OF SOFT SOLDERING.

Reference to fig. 63 will show the purpose of flux in soldering operations. The flux is applied to the surface of the work which must be free from oil, grease or scale, or in other words as clean as possible. As the bit moves along the work, the heat boils the flux, and this boiling action tends to remove the small amount of impurities or oxides that may still be present on the surface of the work. At the same time, a certain amount of gas is given off, and this forms a sort of gaseous shield which helps to prevent the oxygen in the atmosphere combining with the hot surface of the metal. We are already aware of the fact that oxygen will combine readily with hot steel, forming useful coloured oxide films at low temperatures, which are of value when tempering, and severe scaling at high temperatures.

Oxygen will readily combine with most metals, and the presence of an oxide film on the surface of the metal will make successful soldering impossible.

It is clear, then, that the purpose of a flux is to remove and prevent the oxide film on the surface of the metal to be joined.

We now see that as the poker moves along the work, the following sequence of events takes place:

(i) the heat from the poker boils the flux and raises the temperature of the metal surface to that of the molten solder.

(ii) the molten solder "takes" to the pure surface left by the boiling flux, and protected by the gaseous shield.

(iii) the solder solidifies behind the poker.

The soldering operation will, of course, cease when the surplus solder on the poker bit has been consumed.

The speed at which the poker moves along in the direction of arrow A, determines the amount of solder deposited on the surface of the joint, and a skilled tinsmith can solder at a remarkable speed, giving a substantial saving in solder which, because of the tin content, is a relatively expensive metal.

Provided the principles outlined above are observed, good soldering is easily achieved, and very high soldering rates are obtained using automatic equipment where both flux and solder are applied by precision machinery, together with the application of heat. There is little doubt that the design, precision, and amount of engineering skill involved in the machinery and equipment necessary for the soft soldering of "tins" of plums on a mass production basis, would astound most consumers of the products.

Types of Solders

Generally speaking soft solder is an alloy of lead and tin. Lead melts at $327°C$ and tin at $232°C$, and the alloy produced by melting given quantities of both metals will also have a relatively low melting point. The actual melting point will depend on the amounts of tin and lead present and thus the lowest melting point solders would be useful for the mass production of soldered joints, giving a lower cost for the heating process. At the same time, tin is a very expensive metal, about £900 per ton, therefore considerable care is necessary when choosing a particular solder, which will be required in large amounts.

Plumbers' Solder

This will contain about 2 parts lead and 1 part tin, and is used for what is known as a "wiped" joint. It has a definite pasty range, that is to say there is a transitional period between the liquid and solid state, during which the metal remains pasty or plastic. This enables the skilled plumber to wipe or shape the joint as required. This is shown in fig. 64, and is a typical method of joining two lead pipes.

Note the direction of the flow of water, and that one pipe fits into the other to improve the strength of the joint.

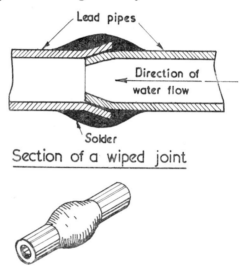

Lead pipes

Direction of water flow

Solder

Section of a wiped joint

FIG. 64.—THE JOINING OF LEAD PIPES.

Tinman's Solder

This will contain about 2 parts tin and 1 part lead, and will, therefore, be more expensive than plumbers' solder. Tinman's solder is always used for poker work because, unlike plumbers' solder, there is no pasty stage between the liquid and solid state. This is very necessary when soldering with a poker, as the solder will solidify immediately behind the poker as it moves along the joint, allowing speedy soldering of the work.

Fluxes

In general two types of fluxes are used when soft soldering. They are known as Active or Passive, the active fluxes having an acid base which helps to clean the job, whilst the passive fluxes demand a very clean surface as they have little or no cleansing action, but prevent oxidisation.

Active Fluxes

A popular active flux is known as "killed spirits". This consists of hydrochloric acid in which some zinc has been dissolved. Glycerine may also be added to reduce the corrosive action of this flux. Such a flux is seldom allowed for the soldering of radio, television components, or aircraft parts because of the dangers of corrosion within the joint. Nevertheless, this flux is most suitable for removing grease or oil from the surface of the parts to be joined, and simplifies the soldering process.

Passive Fluxes

These fluxes have a resin or tallow base, and will be in the form of a stiff paste easily applied to the work. The surfaces of the work must be absolutely clean if the joint is to be successfully achieved, and there is no possibility of corrosion when using this type of flux. For this reason they are always used for electrical work. Resin cored soft solder is obtainable, and this means that the soft solder has its own flux inside it and is most suitable for the rapid joining of small parts using an electrically heated poker.

Sweating

This is the soft soldering process used when large areas require joining, for which the heat given off by a poker would be insufficient. The procedure is relatively simple; both surfaces must be cleaned and "tinned"; they are then placed in correct alignment with a weight on the top part. Heat is then carefully applied around the joint, and when the solder melts the weight will force out the surplus solder and bring the two parts into close contact, the source of heat being removed at this point. Fig. 65 shows a typical application of a sweated joint, consisting of two halves of a brass bearing which, after accurate boring in the lathe, will be reheated and separated for insertion in the bearing housing.

Hard Soldering

We have seen that the process of soft soldering will only make strong joints when certain devices are used to increase the strength of the joint. When only the solder contact is to be used, then the process of hard soldering is adopted, and the first principle of this process is to ensure that there is a maximum area of contact between the surfaces to be joined. The solder is now called spelter, with a much higher strength and melting point.

For the joining of non-ferrous metals such as silver, copper and brass, silver solder is used, whilst steel components are invariably joined by a brass spelter. This process is commonly known as brazing, but essentially it is a form of hard soldering.

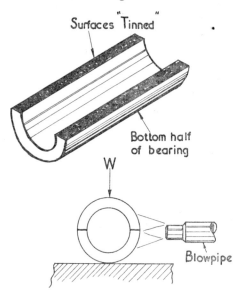

Surfaces "Tinned"

Bottom half
of bearing

W

Blowpipe

Fig. 65.—Sweating Two Halves of a Brass Bearing.

Generally speaking the melting point of silver solder is about 600°C, whilst the spelter used in brazing melts at approximately 850°C. It is, of course, essential that the metals to be joined have a higher melting point than the solder or spelter used to join them, and for this reason the metals having a low melting point are silver soldered when strong joints are required.

The principles of hard soldering are very similar to those of soft soldering. The joints must be clean and free from oil or grease, and the flux used is usually borax.

Reference to fig. 66 will show a typical brazing job. It is essential that the spelter penetrates around the whole area of contact, and this can only be achieved if the temperature of the work is above the melting point of the spelter. Both parts are cleaned and fluxed, and, in general, the smaller the clearance, the stronger the joint will be.

It is a good plan to estimate the amount of spelter required, and to bend the spelter into small rings, placing them in position as shown in fig. 66. Keep the flame of the blow pipe below these spelter rings, and when the temperature of the job exceeds that of the spelter, it will run into the area of contact. A small chamfer will provide a small reservoir for surplus metal, and make a neat job. Under no circumstances should the spelter be heated to run around the top of the job. If this is done the area of contact will be small, and the strength of the joint very low. Fig. 67 shows the importance of maximum area contact.

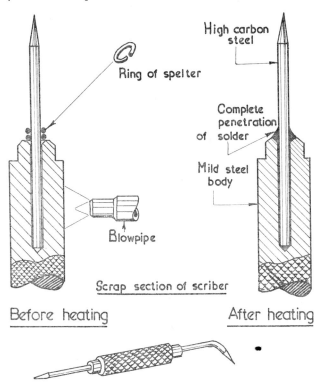

Fig. 66.—The Technique of Brazing Steel.

Summary

It will now be appreciated that the joining of metals involves a wide range of engineering processes and techniques. The engineer is concerned with making sure that the joint produced is sound and well designed and that the method used is economical in terms of equipment needed and time spent in making the joint. With regard to screw thread devices, a thread with a fine pitch will have a stronger tightening action than a thread with a coarse pitch, and for this reason the stud used in fig. 56 will have a Whitworth thread for screwing into the grey cast iron cylinder block, and a British Standard Fine thread to take the mild steel nut. This reduces the risk of stripping the thread in the cylinder block. At the same time, B.S.F. threads are less likely to work loose due to vibration, and they are widely used for all machine tool work and also in motor car and aircraft assembly.

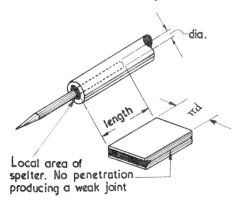

Local area of
spelter. No penetration
producing a weak joint

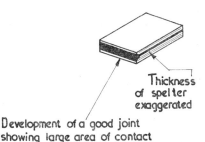

Thickness
of spelter
exaggerated

Development of a good joint
showing large area of contact

Fig. 67.—The Importance of Large Area Contact
in Brazed Joints.

The joining of very small parts, involving the use of small diameter screw threads, is achieved by using British Association threads, and these are available in very small diameters.

The use of screw threads for fastening purposes may be classified as follows:

    (i) B.S.W. for general engineering work,
   (ii) B.S.F. for components subject to vibration, and for good tightening qualities,
  (iii) B.A. for small diameters.

At the present time, increasing use is made of the many types of welding available. These include spot, seam, arc and oxygen-acetylene welding, all of which provide the engineer with a rapid and permanent method of joining metals. The principles underlying these welding techniques will be dealt with in a subsequent volume.

QUESTIONS ON CHAPTER THREE

Part A

1. Make a neat sketch of the following:
    (i) a permanent joint
    (ii) a temporary joint
    using engineering examples.
2. Make a neat sketch of two parts that you would rivet together, giving two reasons for your example.
3. What are the advantages of hot riveting?
4. Make a neat sketch of a typical use for a nut and bolt.
5. What is the difference between a bolt and a set screw? Sketch both.
6. Why are socket screws sometimes used in preference to standard counter-sunk screws?
7. Make a neat sketch showing a typical use for a stud in an engineering assembly. Why is a stud used?
8. Explain the purpose of dowels in an engineering assembly.
9. Give an example of the use of tapers to ensure correct alignment when joining two engineering parts together.
10. Make a neat sketch of two metal components joined by soft solder.
11. What is the purpose of a flux in soft soldering?
12. Under what circumstances would hard soldering or brazing be chosen rather than soft soldering?
13. Sketch two devices that would strengthen a soft soldered joint.
14. What is meant by the soft soldering process known as "sweating"? Sketch a typical example.

Part B

1. Make a neat sketch of an engineering assembly showing two parts joined together in accurate alignment and tightened with four similar screw fastening devices.
2. Why have screw thread fastening devices a V form thread?
3. Write down the approximate composition of the following:
    (i) A soft solder to be used when joining lead pipes.
    (ii) A soft solder to be used for the automatic soldering of food containers.
    (iii) A hard solder to be used for joining silver handles to a silver cup.
    (iv) A spelter to be used for brazing mild steel.
    Give in each case the melting point and the flux used.
4. Make a neat diagram showing how collets are located and tightened into a centre lathe spindle.
5. Show by means of neat diagrams how a machine vice can be located and tightened on a milling machine table.

4 Measurement

WE have seen in the previous chapter that several methods are used to join metal parts together. The success of a joint may depend, not only on the skill and technique of the operator, but also on the accuracy of the mating parts.

The brazed joint, shown in fig. 66, will need a clearance of about two thousandths of an inch between the two mating parts if a really strong joint is to be obtained. Also the use of tapers, registers and dowels will involve working to accurate sizes and dimensions if a high degree of precision alignment is required.

Accurate measurement is an important and sometimes even a vital part of all engineering manufacture, and is, in many cases, the deciding factor as to whether the component is acceptable or not. This means that the engineer, having chosen the best material for the job, decided on the manufacturing processes to be used, and the methods of joining the parts, is now faced with the difficult task of ensuring that the parts are made to the specific sizes laid down in the drawings.

The measurement of any engineering component will involve **three** separate items. These are:

(i) linear measurement.
(ii) angular measurement.
(iii) non-linear functions.

It is a good plan, when meeting any problem of magnitude, first to divide the problem into separate parts, and then proceed to deal with each part in turn. This simple technique is widely used by all skilled engineers and is most applicable when considering the problems involved in the measurement of engineering components. We will, then, take each of the above three items in turn, and examine the principles and techniques involved.

Linear Measurement

All engineering components will have linear dimensions of some kind or another. The length of a bar of metal, the width of a slot, the depth of a keyway, the diameter of a hole, the pitch of a thread, are all examples of linear dimensions. The methods used to determine a linear dimension will depend on the degree of accuracy required. It should be clearly understood that an exact determination of length is not possible when measuring an engineering component, and very accurate measurements will demand a high degree of skill, together with expensive equipment.

Fig. 68 shows a method of determining the height of a component. Let us assume that the height to be measured is 1.3920 ins. Three slip gauges will be chosen, as shown in the illustrated set-up, and a dial indicator set at zero. If now the slip gauges are replaced by the component, and the dial indicator still reads zero, then it is evident that the height of the component can be taken as 1.3920 ins.

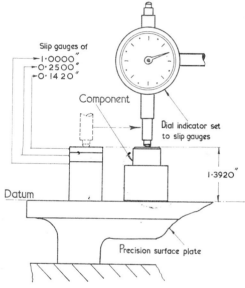

Slip gauges of
1·0000"
0·2500"
0·1420"

Component

Dial indicator set
to slip gauges

1·3920"

Datum

Precision surface plate

FIG. 68.—PRECISE DETERMINATION OF A
LINEAR DIMENSION.

It cannot however, be assumed to be exactly 1.3920 ins. In the first place, the slip gauges will not be of the exact sizes indicated, but will possess a small positive or plus tolerance.

For workshop slip gauges this additional amount of tolerance can be over twelve millionths of an inch per slip gauge. Thus the use of several slip gauges for a set-up of this kind will tend to increase the dimension required. Continual use of slip gauges however will reduce this effect, and will eventually wear the slip gauges below the size indicated.

Secondly, we must be sure that the dial indicator is capable of repeating an exact reading.

Thirdly, it is essential that the surface plate represents a perfect or truly flat surface. Thus the degree of accuracy will depend on the quality and precision of the equipment used. For the example shown, the degree of accuracy would be within one ten thousandth part of an inch.

Most metals will expand when subjected to a rise in temperature, and this means that precise measurement must be carried out under conditions of controlled temperature. Perhaps the most widely used piece of measuring equipment in engineering is the engineers' steel rule.

Engineers' Steel Rule

Irrespective of what equipment we use to measure, the principle involved is the same. The unknown value is determined by comparison with a known standard. This is true for determining the weight of butter, the volume of a pint of milk, or the diameter of a reamed hole.

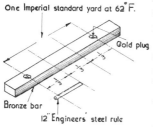

One Imperial standard yard at 62°F.

Gold plug

Bronze bar

12″ Engineers' steel rule

FIG. 69.—THE ENGINEERS' STEEL RULE AS A LINE STANDARD.

An engineers' rule, therefore, is a line standard, and can be considered as a part replica of the Imperial Standard yard which is the basis of all linear dimensions in this country. An Imperial Standard yard is the distance, at 62°F, between two lines engraved on gold plugs set in a bronze bar. Thus the Imperial Standard yard is a line standard. Fig. 69 illustrates the relationship between a 12″ steel rule and the Imperial Standard yard.

For convenience the steel rule is divided into inches and fractions of an inch, but it is important to remember that the Imperial Standard yard is the legal standard of length, and that inches and fractions of an inch are sub-divisions of the distance between the lines engraved on the gold plugs. Remember also that an engineers' steel rule is a measuring instrument and should be treated as such. It should always be kept in a nicely polished condition, and never used as a temporary screwdriver.

Use of the Engineers' Steel Rule

Contrary to popular belief, accurate measurements are possible with an engineers' steel rule, for it is an axiom of craftsmanship that good work is possible with the minimum of equipment. The appreciation, care, and correct use of equipment is the foundation of all craftsmanship, together with due observance of simple principles.

Let us consider the problem of determining the height of a rectangular steel bar, using an engineers' steel rule. It is bad practice to proceed as shown in fig. 70, because an element of error may exist between the rule and the component at the face marked A.

This brings us to our first principle in measurement, and that is, all measurements should be made from a common face, known as a **Datum**.

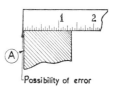

The datum used in engineering workshops is the surface plate or surface table, having a surface of tested flatness. By placing both the component and the rule on the surface plate, the possibility of error at face A is removed and the problem of determining the height of

Possibility of error

FIG. 70.—INCORRECT USE OF ENGINEERS' STEEL RULE.

the component is now confined to the comparison of the edge of the work against the graduations on the rule. This is shown in fig. 71.

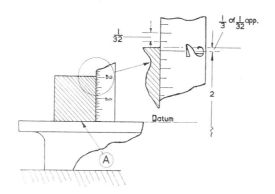

FIG. 71.—CORRECT USE OF ENGINEERS' STEEL RULE.

It is evident that the height of the component is 2″, plus a fraction of 1/32″. The problem is now to determine how much of 1/32″ remains. With practice it is not difficult to estimate this to a remarkable degree of accuracy, and in the illustration we may say that 1/3 of 1/32″ remains. Therefore the total height of the job may now be set down:

$$\begin{array}{r} \textbf{2.000} \\ 1/3 \text{ of } 1/32'' \quad 0.0104 \\ \hline 2.0104'' \\ \hline \end{array}$$

Note that we have separated this problem into separate elements, and the only possible source of error lies in our estimation of the part of 1/32″ that remains. Whilst rules may have graduations of 1/50″, and even of 1/100″, these are of little value, as the lines themselves will be about 4/1000″ in thickness. Graduations of 1/32″ will give best results as we are able to estimate a part of 1/32″, with an accuracy dependent on skill. It may be argued that it is ridiculous to arrive at a figure involving tenths of a thousandth of an inch when measuring with a steel rule, for we have determined the height of the component as 2.0104″.

There is, of course, nothing wrong with arriving at such a figure. Using a steel rule, and following a simple procedure, we have obtained a certain result and that is our assessment of the height of the job. No doubt, another check using a more precise method will reveal a discrepancy between the two results, but this does not change the fact that with the steel rule we obtained the height of the component to the best of our ability. The amount of the discrepancy will be a measure of our skill, and accuracy to within ± .005″ is readily achieved with practice.

Measuring Diameters with a Rule

The measurement of diameters, both external and internal, is another good example of how engineers divide a problem into separate parts. Before commencing to read the rule in order to estimate the diameter of the component shown in fig. 72, it is essential that the reading be taken at the highest point of the component, which will be the diameter. It is difficult to ensure that the rule is at the highest point if the method shown in fig. 71 is used, and calipers are necessary to ensure that the first part of the problem is solved, namely to remove any error caused by measuring a chord and not a diameter.

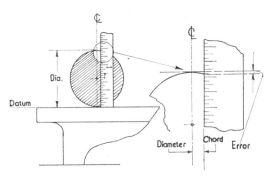

FIG. 72.—POSSIBLE ERROR WHEN USING RULE TO MEASURE
A DIAMETER.

Fig. 73 shows the principle of caliper measurement. The calipers are set so that they just make contact with the work; this means that they are on the exact diameter. The calipers are then transferred to a rule and the reading taken in the manner previously described. The measurement of internal diameters is similar in principle, although more skill is required to ascertain the correct "feel". Note the use of a datum face when reading off the internal calipers, fig. 74. Once again, accuracy to within $\pm$ .005" can be obtained, whilst the mating of one single component to another can be achieved with a high degree of accuracy.

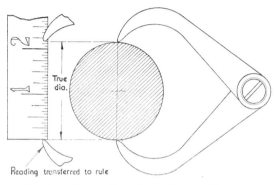

True
dia.

Reading transferred to rule

FIG. 73.—USE OF FIRM JOINT OUTSIDE CALIPERS.

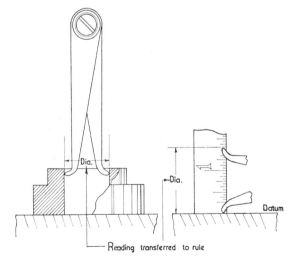

Dia.

Dia.

Datum

Reading transferred to rule

FIG. 74.—USE OF FIRM JOINT INSIDE CALIPERS.

F

Calipers are also useful when measuring components still held on machine tools, for example a component in a lathe or milling machine. This means that the dimension can be accurately measured without removing it from the chuck or vice.

Vernier Calipers

When a linear dimension has to be machined to within $\pm$ .001″, then, it is evident, an engineers' steel rule cannot be used with much confidence. If, however, the problem of estimating a part of a fraction could be simplified to a reasonable degree of accuracy, then the principles previously outlined could be used. This is precisely what vernier calipers do.

Fig. 75 illustrates the application of vernier calipers when measuring the outside diameter of a component. Note that the calipers are actually a steel rule, probably of thicker section, but still a line standard. It has, however, a movable device, on which there is engraved a vernier scale, and provided we can read this scale, it is not difficult to measure to within $\pm$ .001″.

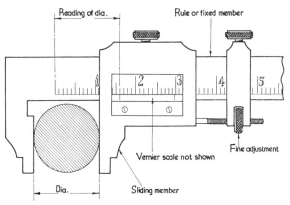

FIG. 75.—VERNIER CALIPERS.

Note the similarity in principle to the use of the rule and calipers; fig. 73.

It can be seen that the vernier calipers are essentially an engineers' steel rule, with a built-in pair of calipers, and fitted with a device that removes the "guessing" of a part of a fraction. The only problem now is that of reading the vernier scale.

The Vernier Scale

We have seen that the purpose of a Vernier scale is to provide a more accurate and reliable method of estimating a part of a fraction.

The principle is illustrated in fig. 76, where the vernier scale will allow accurate readings to 1/100".

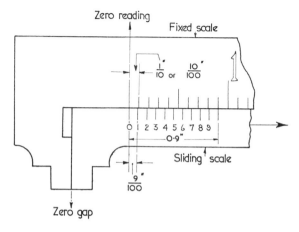

FIG. 76.—PRINCIPLE OF THE 1/100" VERNIER.

Note that the rule or fixed member is graduated in 1/10" or 10/100".

If, now, the width of the first division on the vernier scale is 9/100", then a movement of 1/100" is easily obtained by bringing the first line on the vernier scale to coincide with the first line on the fixed scale. Each division on the vernier scale will also be 9/100", therefore the second line will be 2/100" from the nearest line on the fixed scale. It is evident that the tenth line on the vernier scale will now coincide with a line on the fixed scale.

The accuracy of the vernier scale, therefore, is the difference between the width of the first division on the vernier scale, and the width of the first division on the fixed scale.

The measurement of the diameter of a bar proceeds in the same manner as before. The number of inches is read off, the number of tenths, and now the vernier scale is used to determine the part of a 1/10" that remains. Thus in fig. 77, the reading would be 2.040", made up as follows:

$$2.000$$
$$.040 \qquad 4/100'' \text{ on Vernier scale.}$$
$$\overline{2.040''}$$

Such a vernier scale reading to 1/100" would be of little use in engineering, but verniers reading to 1/1000" are of real value for both measuring and marking out.

The 1/1000″ Vernier

The accuracy of a vernier scale, as previously stated, is the difference between a division on the vernier scale and a division on the fixed scale. In order to read to 1/1000″, this must be the difference between the width of these divisions.

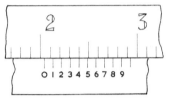

FIG. 77.—1/100″ VERNIER READING 2.040″.

The vernier shown in fig. 78 is used in conjunction with a fixed scale having divisions of 1/20″ or 50/1000″. Therefore the width of our first division on the vernier scale must be 49/1000″, and a movement of 1/1000″ is obtained by bringing the first line to coincide with the first line on the fixed scale. Because the difference is 1/1000″ and there are 50/1000″ in the width of the division on the fixed scale, then 50 divisions will be required before a line on the vernier scale coincides with a line on the fixed scale. Thus the total distance taken up by the sliding scale will be :

$$.049 \times 50$$

$$= \frac{49}{1000} \times 50$$

$$= \frac{49}{20}$$

$$= 2.45″.$$

Perhaps it is as well to admit that the principle of the vernier is not readily assimilated by students, for it is possible to use vernier calipers and yet not fully understand the principle involved. But the use of a vernier is not confined to vernier calipers. There are vernier micrometers, and vernier scales are widely used on rotary tables, dividing heads, barometers, sextants and protractors. It is well worth while to master the principle involved, remembering that it is only a device to remove the "guesswork" involved when an engineer has to estimate a part of a division.

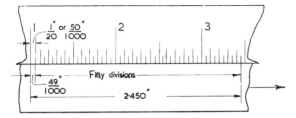

FIG. 78.—PRINCIPLE OF 1/1000" VERNIER.

Micrometers

Although the vernier is an excellent device, there is still the possibility of small errors due to the smallness of the vernier scale causing difficulty in deciding which are the coincident lines.

For greater and more consistent accuracy it is necessary to magnify or enlarge the reading, and this is the principle of the micrometer. Fig. 79 shows a 0—1" external micrometer, having the main parts named. Note that 1/1000" at the anvils is represented by about 1/16" at the thimble. This means that the micrometer has a magnification of approximately 62 to 1. Fig. 79 also shows the method of adjusting a micrometer to zero. A slip gauge of 0.5" width is placed between the anvils which have been carefully cleaned. The ratchet is now used to remove any possibility of the tightening pressure being excessive. It is a good plan to work to the second click of the ratchet, and when this occurs the reading can be examined.

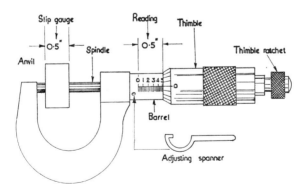

FIG. 79.—ADJUSTING 0—1" MICROMETER TO ZERO.

If the horizontal zero line does not coincide with the zero on the thimble, then adjustment must be made, and this is carried out by using the small C spanner supplied with the micrometer, revolving the barrel until the zero lines coincide. By adjusting the micrometer to zero at its middle reading position we are assured of maximum accuracy throughout the whole range of measurement from o to 1", especially so if all readings are taken at the second click of the ratchet. This principle can be applied to any size micrometer whether external or internal. A micrometer, like vernier calipers, should be treated with great care. When not in use it should be left in its box with the lid closed, and in no circumstances should it be placed on the headstock of a lathe, the table of a milling machine, or left on the bench. With the use of the ratchet to give uniform measuring pressure, which is the equivalent to "feel" when using calipers, accuracy can be achieved to within ± .0002" according to the skill of the user. Greater accuracies are possible with micrometers fitted with a vernier device.

Angular Measurement

It is not generally realised that 90° is an angular measurement. There are very few engineering components that will not have an angle of 90°, and the engineering try-square is an essential and much used measuring instrument. Whenever possible it should be used from a

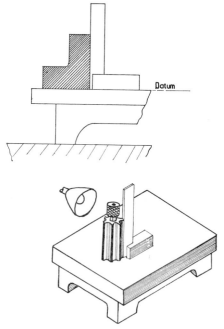

FIG. 80.—USE OF TRY AND MASTER SQUARE.

datum face, and fig. 80 shows a typical application. For more accurate work a master square is used, but this type of square must be used only on a surface plate, whilst a try-square can readily be applied to various parts of a component.

A try-square is a measuring device and must be carefully used, and kept in good condition. It should be checked against a master square at regular intervals. A white light placed behind the square will assist in the testing process, for white light will not penetrate a gap of one ten thousandth of an inch. If white light cannot be seen then the try-square will have a very high degree of accuracy. Such a test is shown in fig. 80.

Components with angles which are not 90° can be measured with an engineers' protractor, which will be calibrated in degrees. Reference to fig. 81 will show that the use of this instrument is somewhat limited, due to its design, and the accuracy obtainable will be somewhere within $\pm \frac{1}{4}°$.

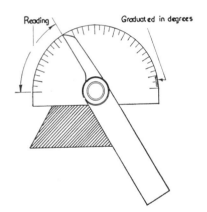
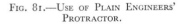
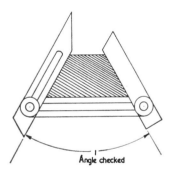

FIG. 81.—USE OF PLAIN ENGINEERS' PROTRACTOR.

FIG. 82.—APPLICATION OF THE UNIVERSAL BEVEL GAUGE.

It is customary to use bevel gauges to extend the use of the engineering protractor, the bevel gauges being set to the protractor and then applied to the work. Fig. 82 shows a typical application, and it is worthwhile noting the similarity of this principle to that of transferring the reading from calipers to an engineers' steel rule. When more precise angular measurement is required then a vernier protractor is used. This instrument can be considered as a logical combination of bevel gauge and protractor, with a vernier device fitted to increase the accuracy. A vernier protractor is shown in fig. 83, with a typical application.

The accuracy of a vernier protractor is 5 minutes of arc, therefore a division on the vernier scale will be 5 minutes away from the nearest line on the fixed scale. Reference to fig. 84 will show that the total arc subtended by the fixed divisions is two degrees or 120 minutes, and this means that the arc subtended by the sliding scale is 115 minutes.

To read the protractor, the zero reading is taken, and this gives a whole number of degrees. Reference to the coincident lines will then give the part of a degree remaining, and this is given to within 5 minutes by the vernier scale.

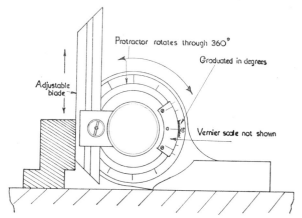

FIG. 83.—THE VERNIER PROTRACTOR.

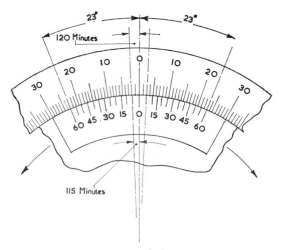

FIG. 84.—PRINCIPLE OF THE VERNIER PROTRACTOR.

Non-Linear Functions

Non-linear functions present the greatest problems in engineering measurement. We may define them as:

    (i) flatness,
    (ii) roundness,
    (iii) parallelism,
    (iv) alignment.

For example, flatness cannot be determined with an engineers' steel rule, and a micrometer would be of little value in determining the roundness of a shaft, because of the very large number of measurements that would be involved.

Let us consider the component shown in fig. 85, taking each non-linear function in turn.

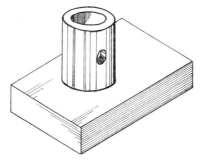

Fig. 85.—Component with Non-Linear Functions.

Flatness

The flatness of the base can be determined by comparison against another surface of known flatness. This follows our original concept of measurement, that is, the comparison of the unknown value against a known standard. A surface plate can be used and the procedure is to smear the surface plate lightly with engineers' blue. The component should be free from sharp edges or burrs, and is moved with even pressure in a figure of 8 movement over the surface plate. Examination of the base will now reveal the areas of contact. If the base is reasonably flat, a uniform blue marking should appear on the surface of the component. Fig. 86 illustrates the technique and possible results.

This is, of course, a practical workshop test of flatness, and the area of marking blue picked up by the component, together with the disposition of the marked areas, allows the practical engineer to form an assessment of the flatness of the base of the component under test.

A uniform marking of about 10 spots per square inch is considered a good standard of flatness, and suitable for good class machine tool work.

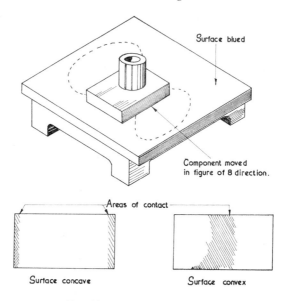

Fig. 86.—Testing for Flatness.

Roundness

A bar turned on a lathe, or a hole drilled in a drilling machine is considered to be round. It is not often that the roundness is measured or checked, because it is assumed that the machine tool used will be capable of producing the work to the degree of accuracy required. The accuracy of any linear dimension must depend on the skill and experience of the operator in his manipulation of the controls and the measuring equipment he will use. We will see, in a later chapter, that the purpose of a machine tool is to produce any given surface, thus a lathe will produce cylindrical or round surfaces, and the accuracy of the roundness, generally speaking, is outside the control of the operator.

If, however, the roundness of a cylindrical component is to be checked, then the following procedure may be used. Three points will determine the diameter of any circle and this is shown in fig. 87. A, B and C are the points, and if AC and BC are joined, bisected, the intersection of the bisectors is the centre of the circle. This means that three points are required to check a cylindrical component, and the practical application of this principle is also shown in fig. 88, where the component is placed on a V block and rotated under a dial indicator. If the pointer remains at zero, then the component is truly round.

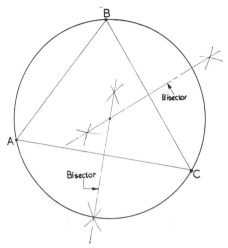

FIG. 87.—THREE POINT PRINCIPLE OF DETERMINING
A CIRCLE.

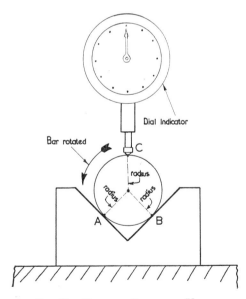

FIG. 88.—TEST FOR ROUNDNESS USING
THREE POINT PRINCIPLE.

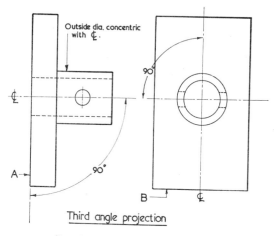

FIG. 89.—NON-LINEAR FUNCTIONS.

Parallelism and Alignment

Examples of these functions are shown in fig. 89. The centre line of the large diameter hole must be 90° to the face A and also 90° to the face B. At the same time, the diameter of the small hole must be 90° to the centre of the large hole, and the checking of these alignments is no easy matter. It will be appreciated that although the linear dimensions may be within the limits laid down, for example the diameters of the holes, the thickness, width and length of the base, the non-linear functions created by these dimensions must also

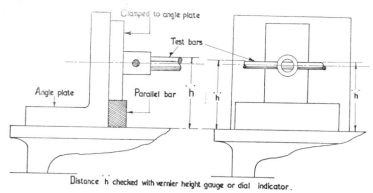

Distance 'h checked with vernier height gauge or dial indicator.

Third angle projection

FIG. 90.—CHECKING NON-LINEAR FUNCTIONS.

be within certain limits. When components are made at the bench, these alignments are most difficult to maintain, and a high degree of skill is involved when hand work is used.

The methods of testing these non-linear functions are shown in fig. 90, and it will be seen that additional equipment is required. The angle plate is used to set components at 90° to the surface plate, and may be L-shaped or box-shaped. They are also available as adjustable types, and can be set so that a component is at a given angle to the surface plate.

Parallel bars are also useful in reducing the area of contact, or raising the component so that checking is made easier. In the set-up shown, absolute cleanliness is essential, and the equipment used must be in good condition, free from damage or burrs.

Marking Out

It is essential that the principles of measurement be understood before any marking out is commenced. The object of marking out is to provide a visual guide, in the form of scribed lines, so that the component can be made to the sizes required, and also possess the necessary alignments.

We have seen that the usual method of checking such dimensions and alignments is to make use of datum faces and additional equipment such as angle plates and V blocks. If, then, we use the same procedure and equipment to mark out the component, we will reduce the possibility of errors which may result in the component being rejected. One can be sure that an inspector or examiner will make full use of all the equipment available, together with the application of measurement principles, in order to determine whether the component is within the limits of accuracy laid down in the drawing. It is, then, a wise plan to regard marking out as a pre-inspection operation, making full use of the equipment available and using the same principles and techniques that will be employed by the inspector or examiner.

Principles of Marking Out

In general two principles of marking out are adopted, dependent on the shape of the component. If the component has several faces, or hole centres at 90°, the best plan is to proceed from two datum faces. This means that one face will be filed flat, and another face filed flat at 90° to the first face. These two faces will be the datums from which all measurements will be made, and the lines scribed from one datum face will be both parallel and at 90° to the lines scribed from the other datum face. Fig. 91 shows a typical component marked out in this way.

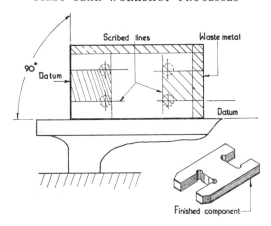

FIG. 91.—MARKING OUT FROM TWO DATUM FACES.

The other principle of marking out proceeds from the use of a centre line as a datum. It is usually employed for components having a curved or radiused profile, for which two datums would offer little advantage, and would represent a considerable waste of effort and time. The example shown in fig. 92, possesses no parallel lines, and the procedure in this case would be to scribe a centre line, and then, using dividers, mark out the respective radii, joining these to give the required profile.

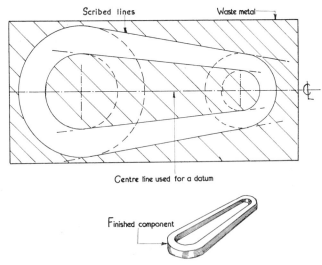

FIG. 92.—MARKING OUT FROM A CENTRE LINE.

Marking Out Equipment

A good scriber is an essential marking out tool. The point, if correctly hardened and tempered, is capable of producing a clean visual line in mild steel. If bright mild steel is used, it is seldom necessary to resort to the use of copper sulphate in order to colour the steel. Whilst the use of copper sulphate may show up a line left by a blunt or badly pointed scriber, it is no substitute for the clear lines possible with a really efficient scriber. It should be necessary to scribe the line only once, firm pressure being used during the length of the stroke. A skilled craftsman will not only file to the line, but will also remove half the line, but this is only possible when working to clean well defined lines. Fig. 93 shows a good scriber, two points being available. The short straight point is used when heavy pressure is required in order to produce clean well defined lines. The longer curved point is used for more precise work, involving greater care and less pressure. In no circumstances should a scriber be sharpened at a grindstone. This practice is almost certain to ruin the tempers and soften the point. The best method is to use an India stone or very fine emery cloth.

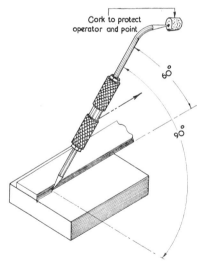

Cork to protect operator and point

60°

90°

FIG. 93.—USE OF ENGINEERS' SCRIBER.

Centre Punches

These are used for two reasons, firstly to provide a point from which to scribe a radius, using a pair of engineers' dividers, and secondly to produce a start for a drilled hole. Two centre punches, then, are required. The first will be relatively slender, and have the point sharpened at 60°. This will provide an accurate location for the divider point and enable clean circles to be scribed. The second centre punch will be of heavier construction, the point sharpened at 90° and can be used to enlarge the centre used for scribing circles, in order to drill a hole. The principles are illustrated in fig. 94.

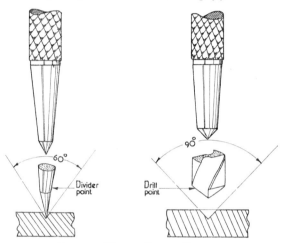

FIG. 94.—USE OF CENTRE PUNCHES.

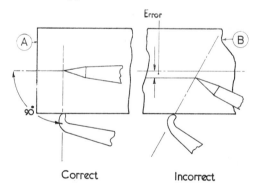

Correct   Incorrect

FIG. 95.—CAUSE OF ERROR WHEN USING ODD
LEG CALIPERS.

Odd Leg Calipers

Care must be exercised when using odd leg calipers. Fig. 95 illustrates the error that can be caused by incorrect use of this marking out tool. For this reason their use is not recommended for accurate marking out; better results are obtained by using a surface plate and scribing block.

Scribing Block

These are invaluable for marking out from a surface plate. The best type has a fine adjustment screw and dimensions are taken off an engineers' steel rule. It is a good plan to keep the scriber horizontal at all times, allowing the minimum length of scriber. This will facilitate the scribing of clean lines, and the line should be scribed only once. More accurate marking out can be done with a vernier height gauge. Fig. 96 illustrates a typical application of a scribing block.

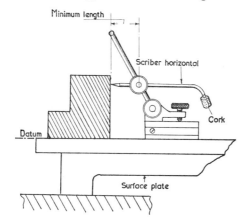

FIG. 96.—USE OF SCRIBING BLOCK FOR MARKING OUT.

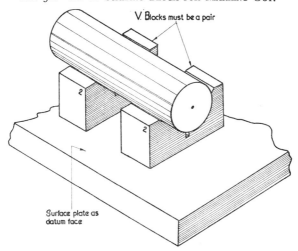

FIG. 97.—USE OF V BLOCKS.

G

V Blocks

These are invariably used for locating or holding cylindrical work. In this way, the three point principle mentioned earlier is observed, and accurate marking out of slots or keyways is usually carried out on V blocks. Fig. 97 shows a typical set-up involving the use of V blocks. It is important to remember that for set-ups of this kind, the V blocks must be a pair, and care should be taken to ensure that the V blocks are always kept as a pair and not interchanged with others.

Summary

The importance of accurate marking out cannot be over-emphasized. The greater the care taken in this stage of manufacture, the less the possibility of subsequent error. The scribed lines represent the **size** or profile of the component and on no account must they be filed or machined out. It is usual, when machining large castings, to employ highly skilled men to do the marking out: the castings are then passed on for machining. This has led to the introduction of centre-dotting the scribed lines as a safeguard to the marker out, in the event of a dispute arising should a dimension be undersize after machining. If the centre dots have been machined below their centres, the machinist is at fault, but if the machining is on the centre of the dots, then the marker out is at fault. This principle is shown in Fig. 98.

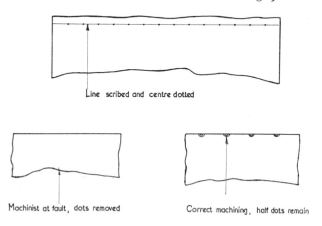

Line scribed and centre dotted

Machinist at fault, dots removed   Correct machining, half dots remain

FIG. 98.—CENTRE-DOTTING A SCRIBED LINE.

For some reason or other this practice has spread to workshops, where the marking out and machining is done by the same operator. For example, the centre-dotting of the profile of the component shown in fig. 92 is both meaningless and wasteful of time and effort. If the part is made from bright mild steel, then it should be quite possible to work to the scribed lines. For greater permanency of the scribed lines there is no objection to making use of the oxide films which form on the surface of polished steel. Polish the bright mild steel plate and heat gently until it turns a dark brown colour. Quenching in oil will give a surface on which a scribed line will show most clearly, and allow accurate filing or machining of the job.

Rough surfaces may be chalked or white washed, and this, perhaps, is an instance when the scribed lines may be centre-dotted at intervals to provide some permanency to the lines. Sharp tools are essential for accurate marking out, and when not in use they should be protected by inserting the points into small corks. The use of a protective cork is also advised when using a scribing block, for this will prevent the possibility of injury when using the scribing block. This is illustrated in fig. 96. There is much satisfaction to be gained when a job has been marked out efficiently and neatly, and this tends to give confidence when the metal has to be removed in order to bring the component to the required shape.

QUESTIONS ON CHAPTER FOUR

Part A

1. Make a neat sketch of an engineering component showing,
    (i)   a linear dimension
    (ii) an angular dimension
    (iii) a non-linear function.
2. Explain why the 1/100" or 1/50" divisions on a rule are of little value when measuring with a rule.
3. Explain what is meant by measuring from a datum face.
4. Sketch an example of the use of a pair of fixed joint outside calipers.
5. Explain the procedure when using an engineers' steel rule to measure the internal diameter of a bored hole.
6. By means of a neat diagram illustrate the principle of a 1/100" vernier.
7. Explain why a micrometer provides a more positive reading than vernier calipers.
8. Show, by means of a diagram, how a 0—1" micrometer can be adjusted to zero.
9. Why is a plain engineers' protractor limited in its use for measuring the angles of an engineering component?
10. Make a neat sketch showing a typical use for a bevel gauge.
11. Write down three non-linear functions, sketching an example of each.
12. How could a small plane surface be tested for flatness?
13. Sketch a typical application of a pair of V blocks.
14. Why is it sometimes necessary to centre dot a scribed line?
15. Sketch two centre punches used in the workshop, giving a typical use for each type.

Part B

1. What is the essential difference between a line standard and an end standard in connection with engineering measurement?

2. Make a neat diagram showing a vernier protractor reading 87° 45′.

3. What is the Imperial Standard Yard?

4. Why is it essential to have a uniform measuring temperature when measuring components to close limits?

5. What are the essential requirements of a pair of engineers' V blocks?

5 Metal Removal at the Bench

THE accurate marking out of a component, as explained in Chapter Four, provides the engineer with the profile of the component together with lines representing slots, or centre dots giving the centres of holes. It is true to state that few components will be brought to shape by the removal of metal at the bench using hand tools, for metal, generally speaking, is tough and considerable force is required to remove it. When large numbers of components are required, it is necessary to use machine tools, which are capable of producing more accurate work at a much higher production speed. There are many instances, however, when components are processed at the bench, and, in general, such work is of a high quality. It may be necessary to replace or repair a single item, which must mate accurately with another part on re-assembly, and this may involve a certain amount of hand fitting. The manufacture of machine tools, jigs, fixtures and gauges, all involves a certain amount of bench work, and the accuracy of the components assembled will be in proportion to the skill and experience of the bench hand concerned.

The engineering student will do well to remember that there is an important and subtle difference between producing components on a machine tool and producing components on the bench. There is no particular merit in just turning a bar of metal down on a centre lathe. If we consider that the lathe costs about £800, and is specifically designed to produce cylindrical work, then the importance of the operator diminishes accordingly. If, however, the operator possesses the skill, knowledge and experience to make the maximum use of the machine tool at his disposal, producing accurate well finished work in the minimum of time, then he re-assumes his importance, and there is little doubt that such men are in short supply at the present moment.

Metal removal at the bench will mean that the bench hand must rely on simple hand tools, and to file a component into a cylindrical shape will call for a very high degree of skill indeed. Added to this, there is the matter of manual effort to be considered, for the machine tool operator has an electric motor which provides the energy required to remove the metal, whilst the bench hand must rely on his own muscular ability. This brings us to our first rule concerning metal removal at the bench, and this is, obtaining the maximum metal removal with the minimum effort.

This is not to say that the craftsman is avoiding work, but merely exercising the very qualities which make him a craftsman by making the best use of the tools at his disposal, and thereby producing accurate well finished work in the minimum of time and, more important, with the minimum of effort. With these thoughts in mind we will consider the more common metal removal tools used at the bench.

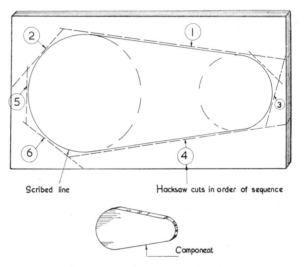

Scribed line   Hacksaw cuts in order of sequence

Component

FIG. 99.—USE OF A HACK SAW.

The Hack Saw

The use of a hack saw is, perhaps, the most rapid way of removing metal at the bench. The great advantage is that for a relatively thin cut, involving small metal removal, a large piece of waste material can be removed in one piece. If we consider the component shown in fig. 99, we see that careful application of the hack saw blade will remove a large area of surplus metal. This is in accordance with our principle of maximum metal removal for minimum effort. If we remember that the metal will still have to be removed down to the scribed lines, then we would do well to perfect a good hack sawing technique and train ourselves to saw consistently to about twenty thousandths of an inch from the line. There is no point in hack sawing carelessly, for this will mean that the metal left by the hack saw must be removed bodily by filing, and this will involve considerable manual effort, for filing is an arduous task, and should be kept to a minimum. It is a wise plan to hack saw always in a vertical direction, placing the component in the vice in such a way that the hack saw cut is truly vertical. Rigid holding of the work is essential, or energy will be lost due to slight bending or vibration of the part, especially if it is of thin material. Fig. 100 illustrates the correct technique. The saw cuts only on the forward stroke, and no pressure is required on the return stroke. Use the full length of the hack saw blade, and see that the teeth point forward away from the handle. If the work is of thick section then conserve your energy by letting the force of gravity do the work for you. In effect, lean on the saw on the forward stroke, allowing the weight of your body to supply the necessary pressure, and not the muscles of your arms.

There is a wide choice of hack saw blades available; 18 teeth per inch is a popular choice but, for sawing thin work, a finer pitch should be chosen to avoid the teeth "snagging" the work.

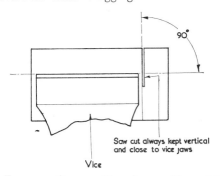

FIG. 100.—CORRECT HACK SAWING TECHNIQUE.

The Use of Files

A file removes metal bodily, that is to say all the metal has to be removed. This is an important point to remember when hack sawing prior to filing. There is, also, one simple principle to remember when filing, and that is, use a rough file for maximum metal removal and a smooth file for accuracy and finish. A rough file will have a coarse pitch of teeth, and though excellent for removing metal is not suitable for obtaining a good finish and close accuracy. At the same time it is foolish to use a smooth file to remove a large amount of metal, as considerable time and effort will be wasted in the process. The object of filing is to bring the shape of the component to the scribed lines, and this is achieved by using a rough file, coming to within about 10 thousandths of an inch of the line. A smooth file is now used to give the required accuracy and finish.

When rough-filing, it is good policy to lean on the file letting the weight of the body do most of the work, but this is not permitted when using the smooth file. Use of the smooth file denotes a finishing operation involving dexterity and skill, and the energy must now come from the arm muscles giving a finer degree of pressure control. As in other techniques there is no short cut or royal road to the art of filing. Experience alone will give filing skill, although perhaps a few simple principles may assist the beginner in his approach to the removal of metal by filing.

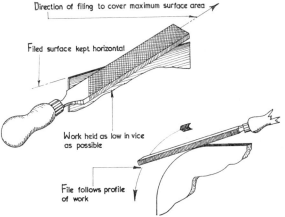

Direction of filing to cover maximum surface area

Filed surface kept horizontal

Work held as low in vice as possible

File follows profile of work

FIG. 101.—TECHNIQUE OF FILING PROFILED WORK.

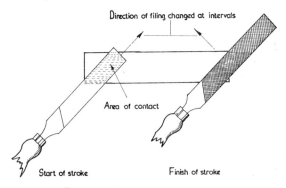

Direction of filing changed at intervals

Area of contact

Start of stroke   Finish of stroke

FIG. 102.—FILING LARGE AREAS.

Generally speaking, filing will involve either the filing of relatively large surface areas, or filing the profile on relatively thin work. The latter presents little difficulty, and the best technique is to keep the file along the length of the work. This is shown in fig. 101. Large areas provide the greatest difficulty, because the non-linear function of flatness is involved. The general principle is to keep the area of contact as large as possible, and to change the filing direction from time to time. This technique is illustrated in fig. 102.

Files

Files are made from high carbon steel, hardened and tempered and available in a large variety of sections and lengths, together with grades of cut. New files should be kept for the softer metals such as copper or brass, and then passed on for use on mild steel, for it is difficult and time consuming to file these soft metals with a worn file. There is no excuse for badly fitted or split file handles, and a file should be used only for filing, and never as a makeshift drift to remove a tapered drill from the spindle of a drilling machine.

The accuracy of filing will depend entirely on the skill of the operator, together with the quality of the marking out. The aim is to file to the line, no more and no less, and thus bring the component to the shape and size required. Much use can be made of the safety edges provided on a hand file. It is bad practice to run one's hand over work which has just been filed as presence of oil or grease on the surface will cause the file rather to slide than cut. A small clean brush should be substituted for an oily or greasy finger.

Scrapers

The use of scrapers is confined to bringing the surface of a component to a high degree of flatness or roundness. They are specially designed to remove only very small amounts of metal, and it is essential that the surface be reasonably flat or round before any attempt is made to scrape it. The main advantage of a scraper is that the metal removal can be very selective, that is to say, small areas of contact can be scraped, as in the method previously described for ascertaining the flatness of a surface by noting the areas that have picked up marking blue from a master surface.

Two types of scrapers are in general use for plane or flat work. They are the pull and push types, illustrated in fig. 103. These are readily made from discarded files, provided the student has a good knowledge of heat treatment. Better results are possible with the pull type. It is essential that the cutting edge be extremely keen, and it is practicable to omit the tempering process, and leave the cutting edge in the dead hard condition.

Sharpening must be carried out on an India stone, and not on an emery wheel, and the edge must be protected when not in use. The

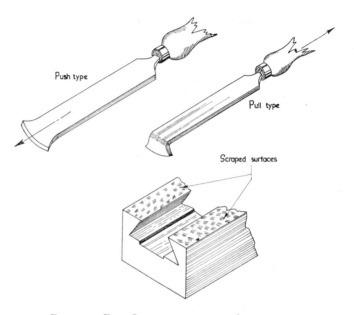

FIG. 103.—FLAT SCRAPERS AND THEIR APPLICATION.

scraping of a large surface area will be a lengthy and costly process, demanding a high degree of skill and patience. Nevertheless, it often is necessary to scrape when two parts have to slide on one another with the maximum area of contact, and yet have provision for the retention of oil between the two surfaces. The indentations left by the scraping action tend to form oil pockets, and this prolongs the life of the moving parts together with the accuracy. This principle is illustrated in fig. 104, and finds much application in the manufacture of machine tool slides and guideways. The same principle also applies when shafts rotate in bearings, and very often the bearing is scraped to ensure maximum area of contact with the shaft, and yet have oil retention properties. The technique is very similar to that of achieving the flatness of a component.

The bearings and shaft are carefully cleaned, engineers' blue is lightly smeared on the shaft, which is then placed in the bearings. The bearing caps are assembled and the shaft revolved twice or three times. On removal of the shaft the areas of contact will be revealed by the blue picked up by the bearing, and these areas are carefully scraped, and the process repeated until the craftsman is satisfied with the final mating surfaces. Half round scrapers are used, and the technique is illustrated in fig. 105.

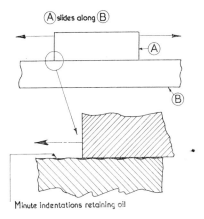

Ⓐ slides along Ⓑ

Minute indentations retaining oil

FIG. 104.—OIL-RETAINING PROPERTIES
OF A SCRAPED SURFACE.

The technique of scraping is perhaps not as difficult as it is often made out to be. Provided the craftsman starts off with a reasonably flat surface, say the base of a simple scribing block, he will find that the removal of the areas of blue contact after application to a surface plate, is not so difficult after all, especially if the cutting edge of the scraper is dead hard. A great deal of patience is required, however, and there is no question of hurrying the work. Some craftsmen are able, by a wrist movement, to finish off the job with a geometrical pattern of scraped marks, but this is not essential though it may look attractive. The acid test is the area of contact per square inch.

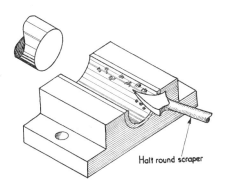

Half round scraper

FIG. 105.—SCRAPING A BEARING.

Cold Chisels

The hardening and tempering of a flat cold chisel was described in Chapter Two, and such a chisel, correctly hardened and tempered, will give many years of good service.

In general four types of cold chisels are in use, each requiring a considerable degree of skill and experience.

Diamond Point

This chisel is shown in fig. 106. It is useful for simple engraving, such as chiselling numbers or letters on parts of machine tool assemblies. It may also be used as a preliminary guide for the chiselling of oil grooves.

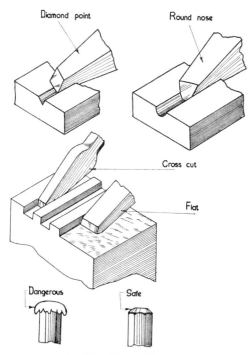

FIG. 106.—THE TYPES, USES AND CARE
OF COLD CHISELS.

Round Nose

Oil grooves are usually chiselled with this type, a typical application is shown in fig. 106.

Cross Cut

This is used for narrow slots, and for breaking down a large area prior to the use of a flat chisel. This technique is shown in fig. 106.

Flat

This is the most widely used cold chisel. It may be used for finishing off work left by the cross cut chisel; taking the heads off rivets; splitting rusted nuts, and cutting sheet metal. Care should be taken when chiselling thin plate as distortion is likely to take place. A hack saw usually is better for dealing with thin plate.

After continual use chisels tend to mushroom at the top, and in this condition they are dangerous as a fragment is likely to fly off when struck with a hammer. From time to time the top should be ground away and a small chamfer ground as shown in fig. 106.

Screw Cutting at the Bench

The removal of metal, in order to produce an external or internal thread, is often carried out at the bench. External threads are produced by stocks and dies, available in different sizes according to the diameter of the thread to be cut. The correct use of a stock and die requires

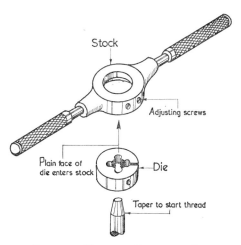

FIG. 107.—USE OF A STOCK AND DIE.

some experience and skill, if a good, well finished thread is to be produced. The principle of roughing and finishing as two separate operations has already been described as an essential process or technique in the production of engineering components, and the stock and die, when properly used, are a good example of this important technique.

Fig. 107 illustrates a stock and die. Note that the die has a split, on both sides of which are two small countersinks. The stock carries three adjusting screws, and tightening of the centre screw will tend to open the die slightly, whilst the other two screws hold the die. In this position the thread will be oversize, and another cut can be taken after slackening off the centre screw and tightening the screws on each side. This will close the die, and so, by careful adjustment and testing with a nut, a good, well finished thread will be produced. The small amount of metal taken off with the finishing cuts will give a good finish. Copious use of whale oil or other lubricant is advised in order to reduce the frictional effects and promote a good finish. A small taper, at the commencement of the thread, promotes axial accuracy.

Taps

Much the same technique is used when cutting internal threads with taps. It is, of course, not possible to adjust a tap, therefore the roughing cut is performed by a taper tap, followed by a second; finally a plug, or finishing, tap is used to bring the thread to size and also give a good finish. The tapping of a hole involves a non-linear function, namely the axis of the tap must be at 90° in all planes to the surface of the work, and this condition is not easy to achieve.

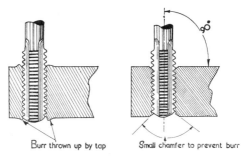

Burr thrown up by tap   Small chamfer to prevent burr

FIG. 108.—TAPPING TECHNIQUES.

It is essential to ensure that the taper tap starts at 90°, and this can be achieved by checking with a try square. Liberal use of a lubricant is essential, and special care is required for blind holes. It is a good plan to drill a small countersink about the depth of one thread to ensure that a burr is not thrown up when tapping the hole. The technique is shown in fig. 108. The experienced craftsman will always use the drill stop to ensure the correct depth, as guesswork is pointless when there is a device fitted on a drilling machine for this very purpose.

The Cutting Action of Hand Tools

All the tools described so far in this chapter remove metal. It is a great pity that they are called "cutting" tools for this is not strictly true. The action of removing metal is one of **shear**, and for this reason they should be referred to as "shearing" tools.

We may divide all shearing, or cutting, tools into two groups. These are:

(i) Single-point tools.
(ii) Multi-point tools.

In all cases the action is the same and, once the principle of shearing has been understood, then it can be applied to any cutting tool used in the workshop, whether at the bench or in a machine tool.

Single-Point Cutting Tools

The cold chisel is a good example of a single-point cutting tool used at the bench. In order to study the action of a cutting tool in removing metal it is essential to consider the tool point as a wedge. In fig. 109 an enlarged view is given of the cutting action of a flat cold chisel.

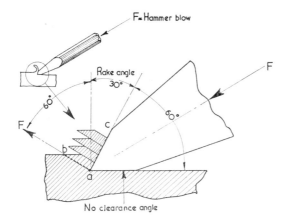

FIG. 109.—SHEARING ACTION OF A
COLD CHISEL.

Note that the heel of the chisel is flat on the work; this ensures that the depth of cut can be maintained. Chisels used on mild steel should have the wedge angle at 60°, and this will give a rake angle of 30°.

The force of the hammer blow F is transmitted at approximately 90° to the cutting face AC, and this sets up a shear stress across the plane AB. Provided the hammer blow is heavy enough, the metal will shear across AB and the chisel will move forward. Because of the ductility of mild steel the shear will not be complete, and the metal will move up the face AC as a continuous chip. This principle is easily shown by a practical demonstration, using a piece of bright mild steel strip about ⅛″ thick. Polish the steel first and place it securely in the vice. Take a cut of about ⅛″ deep, holding the chisel as shown in fig. 110. Striking the chisel top with consistent blows will produce the chip shown in fig. 110, and the shear planes will be clearly seen.

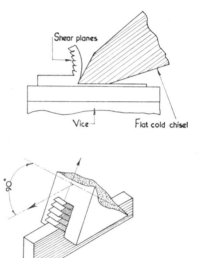

Shear planes

Vice

Flat cold chisel

90°

Pictorial view of shearing action showing wedge principle

FIG. 110.—PRACTICAL DEMONSTRATION OF SHEAR ACTION USING A FLAT COLD CHISEL.

The energy required to shear the metal will be the shearing force along AB, and it is essential to appreciate that this force will be proportional to the length of AB.

This brings us to the most important principle of cutting tools, which is the relationship between the rake angle and the energy necessary to shear or remove the metal. The smaller the rake angle, the greater will be the length of the shear plane, and the greater the energy or effort required to shear the metal. This is shown in fig. 111. The student is strongly advised to master this basic principle, for its application is wide and covers most branches of metal removal involving the use of machine tools.

The wedge action is also shown in pictorial form in fig. 110, and this type of shearing action is known as **orthogonal**, that is to say the face of the cutting edge is at 90° to the line of movement of the tool. It is evident, therefore, that the rake angle on a cutting tool is of great importance, and considerable saving of energy can result from the correct grinding and application of rake angles.

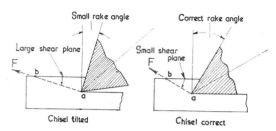

FIG. 111.—EFFECT OF TILT ON EFFECTIVE RAKE
ANGLE OF A COLD CHISEL.

Multi-Point Cutting Tools

We can now consider the filing action, for a file is a multi-point cutting tool having, in effect, a very large number of wedge-like points, each with its own rake angle. The hack saw blade also is a multi-point cutting tool, and the rake angles of these tools are shown in fig. 112.

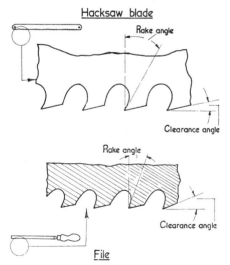

FIG. 112.—RAKE AND CLEARANCE ANGLES ON
HACK SAW BLADE AND FILE.

H

It is necessary to have clearance angles on these wedge-like points, otherwise a large amount of energy would be lost in overcoming the frictional forces set up if there were no clearance.

When using the cold chisel no clearance angle is used, for the loss through friction is small as only one cutting point is in contact with the metal, and the rate of movement of the chisel across the work is very small. It is better to use the chisel as shown in fig. 109, for any loss of energy due to friction at the heel of the chisel is more than compensated for by the maintenance of the depth of the cut. We will see, also, in a later chapter why clearance angles are essential on tools used for metal removal on machine tools. It should be understood that the clearance angle takes no actual part in the cutting or shearing action, but is ground on the tool to remove the loss of energy caused by frictional resistance. So important is the rake angle that every effort is made by engineers to provide all hand tools with this important angle, and many ingenious devices are used. The rake angle on a tap used for cutting internal threads is a good example, for taps are hardened and tempered, are of relatively small cross-section and are easily broken if excessive torque or turning moment is applied.

The rake angles on the flutes will reduce the shear planes so that less torque is required to shear the metal. It must be remembered that there is no clearance angle on hand taps, and that the frictional forces set up will increase the torque and tend to cause breakage.

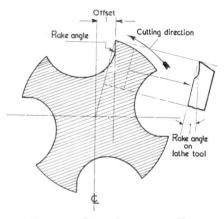

FIG. 113.—RAKE ANGLE ON A TAP.

Fig. 113 shows a cross-section of a tap, and it will be seen that the rake angle is obtained by offsetting the flutes. If the flutes were machined, so that the cutting faces were radial, then there would be no rake angle, and such a tap would have a poor cutting action. The dies used to cut

external threads are also supplied with a rake angle, and this is obtained
by the position of the four holes as shown in fig. 114.

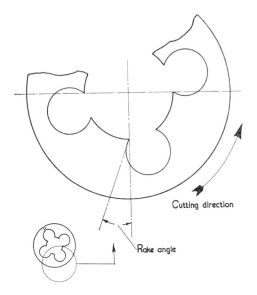

FIG. 114.—RAKE ANGLE ON A DIE.

Summary

Metal removal at the bench, as we have seen, is mainly concerned
with sawing, filing, scraping, chiselling and the threading of drilled
holes or round bars. In each case manual or muscular effort is involved
together with the difficulty of maintaining accurate linear and non-
linear functions. The removal or shear of the metal is greatly facilitated
by the provision of rake and clearance angles on the hand tools used,
and the wedge action forms the basis of the shearing action. In general,
the softer or more ductile the metal, the greater the rake angle, although
brass and grey cast iron are exceptions to this rule. It is a general
principle also that the clearance angle is kept to a minimum; in the
case of a flat cold chisel no clearance angle is necessary. It follows,
therefore, that the sharpening of hand tools at the grindstone is an
important process, care being required not to ruin the temper of a high
carbon steel tool, and also maintain the correct rake angle. To remove
metal from large surface areas is, evidently, a difficult task if hand
methods are to be employed, whilst the maintenance of accurate linear
dimensions and non-linear functions becomes an almost impossible
task.

Nevertheless a basic knowledge of the fundamental principles of metal removal by hand tools is essential to those who aspire to technician status, for it will give an indication of the problems involved and the high degree of skill, patience and experience which are necessary if accurate and well finished work is to be produced.

The preceding chapters have dealt with the principles and techniques associated with good-class hand or bench work. It cannot be too often emphasized that engineers are concerned with shaping or forming metals, choosing the best metals for the job, and the most economical method of production to ensure both quality of product and quantity of production.

There is little doubt, that of all the occupations available, engineering offers the greatest opportunities, not only in the numerous avenues of advancement, but also in the personal satisfaction or pleasure enjoyed by all true craftsmen or technicians in the completion of a well finished and accurate piece of work. This can only be achieved by accurate and clean marking out, sawing or filing with care and skill, the correct use of joining principles to produce sound and reliable joints, together with cutting tools accurately hardened and tempered, and ground to the correct angles.

Whilst it is true to say that machine tools tend to replace the craftsman, it is still necessary to use the machine tools to the best advantage, and this is only possible if the principles underlying the design and application of machine tools are understood and appreciated.

QUESTIONS ON CHAPTER FIVE

Part A

1. Write down the names of **three** tools used to remove metal at the bench.
2. Why is it important to hack saw as closely as possible to a scribed line?
3. Make a neat sketch illustrating **two** important points to be observed when using a hack saw.
4. Why is it necessary to have both rough and smooth files?
5. Make neat sketches showing the cross-section of three different files.
6. Why is it difficult to produce a flat surface when using a file?
7. Make a neat sketch of a flat scraper. What is the purpose of scraping?
8. Why are three taps used for cutting an internal thread?
9. Why is it desirable to use a cutting medium when tapping holes?
10. What is the purpose of the three screws in a die holder?
11. Sketch a cross-cut cold chisel, showing a typical application of its use.
12. Show, by means of a sketch, the rake angle on a cold chisel. Why is this rake angle important?
13. What is the essential difference between a single-point and a multi-point cutting tool?
14. Show, by means of a diagram, the rake angle on a tap.

Part B

1. An inch diameter tap is to have a rake angle of 12°. What should the offset be, when milling the flutes?

2. Describe, briefly, how a shaft could be bedded into a brass bearing.

3. Show, by means of a neat diagram, the rake angle on a twist drill.

4. What improvement could be effected to increase the oil retaining properties of two bearing surfaces after they have been scraped? (**Hint:**—a cold chisel would be used.)

5. Why is it advisable to keep new files for use on metals such as brass or copper? What file would be used for aluminium?

6 Machine Tool Principles

A MACHINE tool can be described as a power driven device, which will produce a desired surface. It is important to appreciate that engineering components usually are of geometrical shape or a combination of geometrical surfaces. This important fact is illustrated in fig. 115 which shows a typical engineering component.

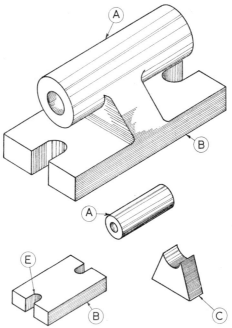

FIG. 115.—GEOMETRICAL BREAK-DOWN OF AN
ENGINEERING COMPONENT.

If we break down this component into separate parts we will find that, in each case, the part is of geometrical shape, having a geometrical surface. For example part A has an external cylindrical surface together with an internal cylindrical surface which is, of course, the bored hole.

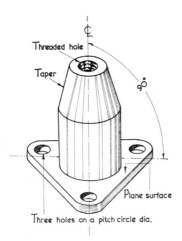

Threaded hole

Taper

90°

Plane surface

Three holes on a pitch circle dia.

FIG. 116.—ENGINEERING COMPONENT WITH
DIMENSIONS CONTROLLED BY A CENTRE LINE.

Part B has plane surfaces, together with part cylindrical surfaces which are the radii of the slots at E. The part C also has plane surfaces, two of which are at an angle. It is possible to produce this component by making the separate parts at the bench and welding them together, but this would entail a very large amount of effort, time and skill, and would be an almost impossible task. There are, also, other geometrical surfaces which are exceedingly difficult to produce by hand methods. Fig. 116 shows an engineering component, comprising plane surfaces, cylindrical surfaces, conical and helical surfaces. Conical surfaces are more commonly known as tapers, whilst a helical surface or form is, evidently, a screw thread. The non-linear functions of this component will evolve around the centre line of the component.

The centre line can be considered as an imaginary datum, and thus it is not possible to produce this component accurately at the bench for this very reason. It is difficult enough to work from a datum face, as we have seen in the previous chapter, and to expect accuracy by working from a line which exists only in theory is asking the impossible. Much the same problem faced the potters who were concerned with the manufacture of clay utensils several thousands of years ago. Yet the shaping of clay is relatively easy, for the hand of the potter is the tool for this purpose. We can regard the manufacture of pottery as one of the first engineering accomplishments of mankind using a form of machine tool which, in this instance, was the potter's wheel.

Let us consider the problem of shaping the utensil shown in fig. 117. The shape is evidently geometrical, consisting of a combination of spherical and cylindrical surfaces, and the machining of this component, say from a solid block of aluminium on a centre lathe, would present a severe problem even to the most skilled of turners. A very simple expedient was, however, adopted by the early potters, and this principle is still the basis of most machine tool design and construction.

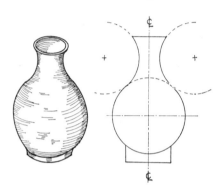

FIG. 117.—GEOMETRY OF A CLAY UTENSIL.

This principle is known as **generating,** whereby a desired geo-metrical surface is achieved by the summation or combination of geometric forms. Perhaps the method adopted by the potters will make this a little clearer. The clay was first rolled into cylindrical rods, between the palms of the hands. A series of circles was then made up, their diameters varying according to the shape of the utensil required. These circles were then placed in position, smoothed over, and the utensil baked or fired to provide the necessary hardness. This principle is shown in fig. 118, and it can be seen that cylindrical, conical and helical forms can readily be produced in this way. This principle was used by engineers during the 16th Century to make gun barrels. The procedure was to wrap wrought iron wire around a cylindrical form, and then weld the wire at the outside, thus producing an iron cylinder. Screw threads were also produced in a similar manner. A length of wrought iron wire would be accurately wrapped around the component to be threaded, a simple template being used to ensure correct spacing of the wire, thus giving a constant pitch. A diamond pointed chisel would then be used alongside the wire, and the thread started in this manner.

Ingenious though these methods were in producing geometric shapes or surfaces, they take no account of the fact that the accuracy of the form produced is governed by the relationship of the outside surface to the centre line of the work. This must have been appreciated by the early potters, for it led to the introduction of the potter's wheel.

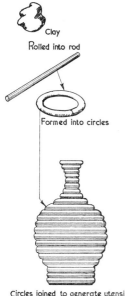

Clay

Rolled into rod

Formed into circles

Circles joined to generate utensil

FIG. 118.—GENERATING A CLAY UTENSIL BY HAND.

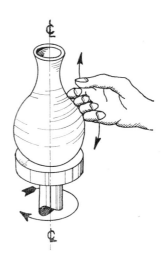

FIG. 119.—GENERATING ON A POTTER'S WHEEL.

It has been said that the lathe is the father of all machine tools, but this is not strictly true. The potter's wheel preceded the lathe, and is almost certainly the earliest example of generating by semi-mechanised methods. The principle of the potter's wheel is still embodied in most of our machine tools at the present time, and its importance is such that it is worthy of closer inspection. Fig. 119 illustrates the principle involved. Note that the utensil now revolves around its centre line, and that the movement of the potter's hand, at the points of contact, produces a surface that is equidistant from the centre line, and thus geometrically accurate. It is essential, of course, that the wheel revolves and that the centre line of the pot is in alignment with the axis of rotation. These are precisely the conditions that are required in a centre lathe, except that the potter's hand is replaced by a cutting tool that will remove the metal by a shearing action.

Generating

We may now consider the essential conditions necessary to "generate" a cylindrical surface on a centre lathe. It must be appreciated that these conditions are essentially geometric, and the accuracy of the cylindrical surfaces produced will be in direct proportion to the geometric accuracy built into the lathe. In order to generate a true cylindrical surface, it is essential, as shown in fig. 120, that the tool moves along a path parallel to the centre line of the work in **two planes.** This means that the tool point must move so that distance X and distance Y are constant. Each revolution of the work will generate a true circle and the movement of the tool will produce a series of circles which will, in effect, represent a true cylindrical surface. It would, of course, be a great advantage if the tool could also traverse at 90° to the centre line, for this would enable true cylinders to be turned and this principle is shown in fig. 121. At the same time, a lathe that could only produce or generate cylinders would have a limited use, for conical or tapered

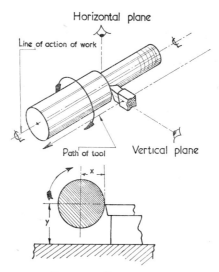

FIG. 120.—CYLINDRICAL.

surfaces are also required in engineering. The conditions for producing a conical surface are shown in fig. 122. The path of the tool must still be in the same horizontal plane as the centre line of the work but it will not be parallel to it in the vertical plane. The amount of deviation will determine the amount or angle of taper produced. Thus the taper is generated, the progressive movement of the tool away from or towards the centre line of the work generating circles of increasing or decreasing diameter respectively.

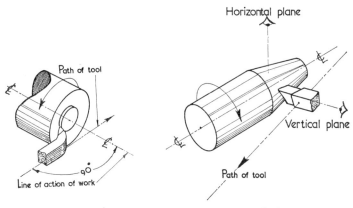

FIG. 121.—PLANE.　　　　　FIG. 122.—CONICAL.

The generation of helical forms or screw threads on a centre lathe differs in no way from the method shown in fig. 120, for it must be realised that the cylindrical surface produced is actually a helical form or screw thread with a very fine pitch. Screw threads, however, have relatively large pitches, and as a pitch is a linear dimension, it is essential that the tool moves a precise distance for each revolution of the work. This will mean that provision must be made for accurate linear movement of the tool for each revolution of the work, the amount of linear movement depending on the pitch of the thread to be cut.

These are the geometric and dimensional problems involved in the generation of the various shapes discussed. The practical application of these principles calls for great skill and ingenuity in the design and construction of centre lathes.

Generating Plane Surfaces

Plane surfaces are widely used in engineering and the production of these plane surfaces by hand methods is a tedious and expensive matter, especially when large areas are involved. A plane surface will also have the non-linear function of flatness, together with the certainty of adjacent faces at 90°, and these conditions govern the design of most machine tools used to produce plane surfaces. The principle involved has been known to mankind for several thousands of years, and, like the potter's wheel, is worthy of further consideration.

Fig. 123 illustrates a raft made a very long time ago. If we assume that the length of the raft is 18 feet, and breadth 12 feet, then the manufacture of this flat rectangular piece of wood would have proved an impossible task for the primitive ship builders or engineers. The diameter of the tree used would have to exceed 20 feet, and with the simple hand tools at their disposal, they would be unable to produce the body of the raft in one piece.

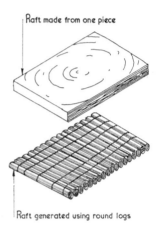

Raft made from one piece

Raft generated using round logs

FIG. 123.—MANUFACTURE OF
A WOODEN RAFT.

The problem was solved by generating a plane surface using uniform logs of smaller diameter, and lashing them tightly with ropes. The surface thus produced is not truly flat, but it can be considered as a plane surface, and would allow the building of a small hut on the surface. At the same time the problem of manufacture would be simplified to a very great degree.

Much the same principle applies in modern workshop engineering. A small shaping machine will produce a plane surface with relative ease, whilst to produce a similar plane surface by hand methods would increase the cost and production time a hundredfold. The principle of generating a plane surface on a shaping machine is shown in fig. 124, and it differs little from that of generating a plane surface for a raft. As the tool moves forward it shears the metal, and on the return stroke, the work is advanced along the direction of arrow A. Thus another strip of metal is removed in the forward movement of the tool along the direction of arrow B, and the continuation of this process will generate the plane surface C. Note that the flatness is one of degree

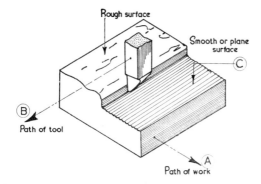

FIG. 124.—GENERATING ON A SHAPING MACHINE.

only, and will be dependent on the shape of the tool point, and the rate of movement of the work, more commonly known as the 'feed'. Once again we have two lines of action:

(i) the path of the tool,
(ii) the path of the work,

and, like the lathe, the accuracy of the work produced will depend on the geometric relationship between these two lines of action. We can, then, define "generating" as the effect produced by the intersection of two lines of action. As the most widely used angle in engineering is 90°, it is almost certain that these lines of action will be at 90° if the machine tool is used to generate a plane surface.

The conditions for the production of accurate work on a shaper are shown in fig. 125, and once again the practical applications of these movements provide the engineer with many problems. The distance a from the tool point to the table must be a constant, both in the front and side elevations, if parallel surfaces are to be generated, and these conditions must be maintained irrespective of the table position and the tool position. These geometric alignments are of great importance and apply equally to milling machines, drilling machines and indeed all machine tools that "generate" a surface.

Perhaps the art of machining can be described as the best utilisation of the geometric movements available on the machine tool, and we shall see in the following chapters how the skilled machinist uses his machine in the best way to produce a product of the desired shape and size.

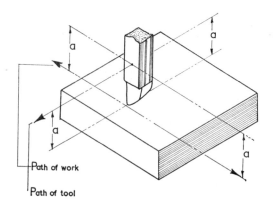

Path of work

Path of tool

FIG. 125.—GEOMETRY OF WORK AND TOOL
MOVEMENTS.

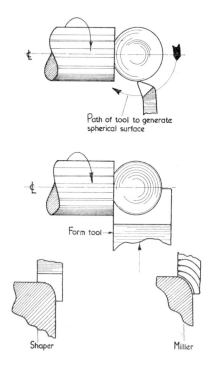

Path of tool to generate
spherical surface

Form tool

Shaper

Miller

FIG. 126.—APPLICATIONS OF FORMING.

Forming

Forming is another method of producing a required surface. The principle of forming is relatively simple, and consists of providing the desired form on the cutting tool and feeding it into the work. The shape produced on the work will be similar to the shape of the tool, and this principle is sometimes known as 'copying'. It will, of course, still be necessary to revolve the work, for example, when forming on a lathe, for power is needed to shear the metal, and the work must have sufficient torque to bring about the shearing action. At the same time the tool must be fed in to the required depth, but the fact still remains that the surface or form produced is a replica of the form on the tool. Fig. 126 shows a component with a spherical head, and to generate this shape would mean that the tool would have to move along the path indicated by arrow A. Such a path would call for a complicated piece of mechanism, but, provided the spherical portion is fairly small, it is much easier to form it, as illustrated in fig. 126; which also shows the application of "forming" on a milling and shaping machine.

Essentials of Machine Tools

The cost of metal in a watch would be about two shillings, but no watch can be purchased at this attractive price. Watches are very similar to machine tools in one respect, in that the cost will be directly proportional to the accuracy required.

A watch incapable of keeping accurate time would be of no practical use, and this is equally true for a machine tool incapable of producing work within desirable limits of accuracy. A machine tool, known as a jig borer, and capable of drilling holes having their centres to a linear accuracy of one tenth of a thousandth of an inch, can cost over fifteen thousand pounds, which is an indication of the price of accuracy in connection with machine tools. This accuracy, as we have seen, is related to the geometric movement of either the tool or the work, and knowledge of the practical methods adopted in obtaining these movements is important.

Sliding Faces or Guideways

If we reconsider the action of generating a cylindrical surface on a centre lathe, then it can be seen that it is necessary to ensure that the tool moves along a path parallel in two planes to the centre line of the lathe. This problem, involving the sliding of one part in accurate alignment with another is common to most machine tools, and the method adopted is to use sliding faces or guideways. Fig. 127 shows a section through a typical lathe bed, with the saddle in position. Note carefully that the saddle locates only on the guideway G and the sliding face S; there is clearance everywhere else.

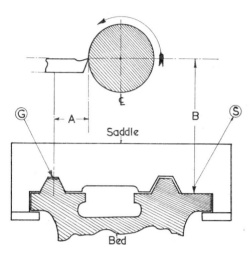

FIG. 127.—USE OF GUIDEWAYS AND BEARING
SURFACES.

We may consider the tool as part of the saddle, thus the guideway G controls the constancy of the dimension A, whilst the surface S controls the dimension B. Provided then that both the guideway G and the surface S are parallel to the centre line of the lathe, in their respective planes, the path of the tool will possess the geometric conditions necessary to generate a cylindrical surface. This principle is shown clearly in fig. 128, which includes also the location for the tailstock, which uses the opposing guideway and sliding surface. Note that the distance between the guideway and the sliding surface is at a maximum, and that this promotes greater stability. When cutting metal on a lathe the cutting force acts downwards, and this is an advantage when inverted V guideways are used. Fig. 129 shows that the force W has the effect of giving closer, and thus more accurate, bearing contact on the guideways.

Much the same principle is used for the cross slide and compound slide. The purpose of the cross slide is to ensure that the path of the tool is at right angles to the centre line of the lathe, thus allowing the ends of bars to be faced. The compound slide may be set at a required angle, the path of the tool generating a conical surface, but it is still essential that the tool moves along a straight line. The most widely used device is the dovetail slide, and this is illustrated in fig. 130.

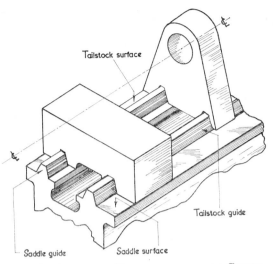

Tailstock surface

Tailstock guide

Saddle guide   Saddle surface

FIG. 128.—SADDLE AND TAILSTOCK GUIDING ON A CENTRE
LATHE.

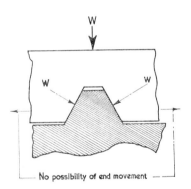

W

W   W

No possibility of end movement

FIG. 129.—ADVANTAGES OF THE
INVERTED V GUIDEWAY.

It will be seen that the only movement possible is along the direction
of arrow A, and because of the angle of the dovetails the sliding portion
B cannot lift from the fixed part C. The three adjusting screws at the
side are used to exert pressure on the gib D, in order to take up any
wear which may take place on the sliding surfaces. This principle of
the dovetail slide is very widely used in machine tool construction;
examples are to be found in shaping, milling, planing and slotting
machines. The scraping of the bearing surfaces of these slides is a good

I

example of the necessity for accurate bench work for the production of high precision equipment. Because this type of slide is invariably used for feeding the cutting tool to the required depth in most of the machine tools described above, it is important that the student understands the principle involved.

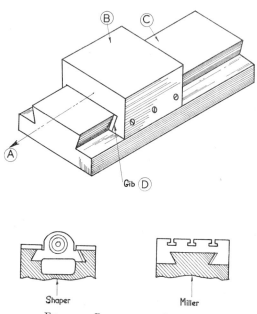

Gib D

FIG. 130.—PRINCIPLE AND APPLICATION OF THE DOVETAIL SLIDE.

The sliding member receives its movement through the rotation of a lead screw, which is constrained within the fixed member. Thus for one complete revolution of the lead screw, the sliding member will have a linear movement equal to the pitch of the thread. This thread is not used for tightening purposes, but merely to transmit motion, and will have a square or Acme form.

If now a dial is rigidly fixed to the lead screw, and suitably calibrated, then small linear movements of the tool are possible by working to a zero line on the fixed member. The dial is usually referred to as an indexing dial, and represents one of the most valuable devices on a machine tool. Tool movements of one thousandth of an inch are readily achieved, although whether the tool will remove this small amount of metal will depend on the condition and accuracy of the machine tool.

The principle is illustrated in fig. 131, and the student is strongly advised to use this valuable device whenever possible, for it enables him to achieve a higher degree of accuracy than would otherwise be possible.

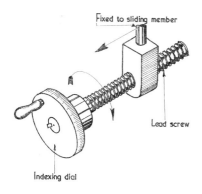

Fixed to sliding member

Lead screw

Indexing dial

FIG. 131.—PRINCIPLE OF LEAD SCREW AND INDEXING DIAL.

Transmission of Motion

We have seen that the movements of both tool and work along prescribed paths are the fundamentals of producing parts on machine tools. The means by which these movements are produced are of considerable interest, and some knowledge of them is necessary if the student is to understand the design, construction and operation of machine tools.

Spur Gears

These are generally used to transmit motion in parallel planes. For purposes of calculation and design, a spur gear can be considered as a circle, which is known as the pitch diameter of the gear. Gears provide a positive, non-slip, drive and have replaced the old fashioned method of using leather belts. V belts, however, are still used, especially in the transmission of motion and power from the electric motor to the lathe headstock. The use of belts allows fairly great distances between the driving and the driven units, and a further advantage is that the belt may slip should the load be excessive. The use of gears means that great care must be taken to avoid severe overloading, for example running the saddle up against the headstock of a lathe whilst on automatic feed. Should this happen then there is a real danger of severe damage to the gear box of the lathe, although many machine tools are fitted with shear pins which will shear under excessive load and thus prevent severe damage to the gear box. The principle of spur gears to transmit motion in parallel planes is shown in fig. 132, together with the shear pin principle. Note that speed ratios can easily be changed by varying the number of teeth on the gears.

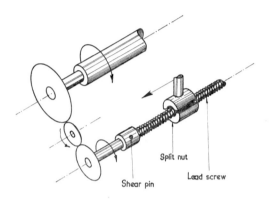

Split nut

Lead screw

Shear pin

FIG. 132.—APPLICATION OF SPUR GEARS.

The illustration shows a simple lathe, the spur gears providing parallel motion of the saddle to the centre line of the lathe, through a lead screw. The lead screw is similar in all respects to the lead screws used in the dovetail slides previously described, except that the rotation is now brought about by spur gears, which transmit motion from the lathe spindle. The accuracy of the pitch of the lead screw thread is of great importance if accurate threads are to be cut on the lathe.

Bevel Gears

These are used to transmit motion at any particular angle, although 90° is the most common example. The principle is shown in fig. 133, and illustrates the method used to raise the table of a milling machine. Note, once again, the use of a lead screw. The two gears are in effect the frusta of cones, which are made to rotate in such a way that the relative position of the teeth in contact remains constant.

Rack and Pinion

The use of this device allows circular motion to be transmitted into linear motion, and is the method used on most lathes to traverse the saddle along the bed of the lathe by hand. The principle is shown in fig. 134. The linear movement of the rack is determined by the pitch of the pinion together with the amount of rotation of the hand wheel.

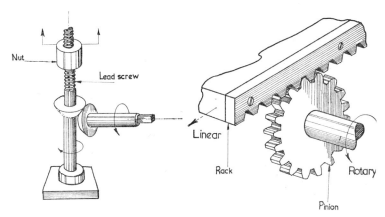

Nut

Lead screw

Linear

Rack

Pinion

Rotary

FIG. 133.—APPLICATION OF
BEVEL GEARS.

FIG. 134.—THE RACK AND PINION.

These are only some of the devices used in machine tools to transmit motion and power. Perhaps it will now become evident that the manufacture of gears, racks, pinions and lead screws is well beyond the range of work possible at the bench using hand tools, for if the above items are to be of any practical value they must possess very accurate linear dimensions and non-linear functions. The accuracy of a machine tool in producing a given surface is related not only to the accuracy of the sliding surfaces, but also to the accuracy of the various methods employed to bring about the motions of the tool and work.

Summary

Machine tools play a very important part, not only in our engineering industry, but also in our national economy. They are to be found in almost every industry for they produce work at a speed and precision not possible by hand methods. They are the logical outcome of engineering skill, knowledge and experience, and it has taken mankind many thousands of years to bring them to their present state of perfection.

With regard to their use in engineering workshops, their primary purpose is to produce a desired geometrical surface, and this is achieved by the process of "generation". Small surfaces may be produced by the "forming" or "copying" process. Generally speaking, most movements will be parallel to or at 90° to the work, together with an upward or downward vertical movement. The linear accuracy of the components produced is greatly assisted by the use of indexing dials, and the rate of feed of the work or tool is readily altered by the use of gears.

Most machine tools remove metal in the process of generating. The principles of machining are very similar to those adopted when removing metal at the bench. Firstly, absolute rigidity is essential; the work as well as the cutting tool must be securely held. Secondly, the principle of roughing and finishing should be adopted. The object of roughing is to obtain maximum metal removal in the minimum time. Usually low speeds are used for "heavy" cuts and higher speeds for "finishing" cuts. Accuracy of dimensional control and finish is of secondary importance when roughing, for sufficient metal must always be allowed for the finishing operation.

Finishing involves bringing the work to the required dimensional accuracy with the quality of finish specified. The speed of the work or tool is usually increased and the feed diminished. The metal removal will be small thus reducing the bad effects of distortion and vibration often set up when very heavy cuts are taken. As far as possible as much machining as possible should be carried out with **One** setting of the work. This is a most important principle when using machine tools, the object being to take advantage of the various geometrical alignments built into the machine tool, such as the ability to produce parallel faces, or faces at 90° to each other. Some machine tools in common use in most workshops are listed below, together with the types of surfaces produced.

The Centre Lathe

The centre lathe is mainly used for the production of single cylindrical components. Tapers, screw threads and bored holes are also produced. Considerable setting and skill are required if accurate parts are to be produced, much of the turners' time being taken up with tool changing and setting. Linear accuracy is dependent on the skill and experience of the operator in using the index dials and measuring instruments to check his work. The accuracy possible will also be determined by the quality and condition of the lathe. Generally speaking, linear dimensions to within plus or minus half a thousandth of an inch are only possible with the more expensive type of lathe.

Capstan Lathe

The capstan lathe is similar in principle to a centre lathe, but is fitted with a hexagonal turret or capstan which provides **Six** additional tool positions. Thus most capstans have eleven tool positions compared with five on a centre lathe fitted with a 4-way tool post. Dimensional accuracy is controlled by the use of positive **stops,** and, in this way, a capstan setter can set the tool positions and stops and thus allow a semi-skilled operator to produce the component by working to the stops. In this way the capstan operator is continually producing components whilst the setter will have several machines to look after.

This, of course, follows one of our stated principles of doing as much machining as possible at one setting, whilst the principle of roughing and finishing is readily achieved by the relatively large number of tool positions. Generally speaking, linear accuracy will be to within plus or minus one thousandth part of an inch, according to the size of component and quality of the capstan lathe, as well as the skill and experience of the capstan setter.

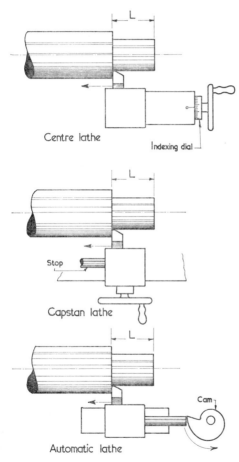

Centre lathe

Indexing dial

Stop

Capstan lathe

Cam

Automatic lathe

Fig. 135.—Development of Linear Control on Lathes.

Automatic Lathe

As the name suggests these lathes are automatic in operation. Whilst the use of stops in a capstan lathe allows a semi-skilled operator to produce components without the aid of the skill and experience necessary when using indexing dials and measuring instruments, the use of cams now replaces the operator. The lathe is set by the lathe setter who adjusts the cams to produce the linear dimensions required. Provided the automatic lathe is supplied with material, usually in the form of long bars, then it will produce components without any need for an operator. This is an important step in machine tool utilisation, for the human element plays a most important part in precision engineering. Human beings are subject to many shortcomings; fatigue, boredom and loss of concentration, are all common factors that tend to influence the ability of an operator to produce accurate work.

A well made, accurate, case-hardened mild steel cam will control the linear movement of a cutting tool with precision and unerring accuracy, and will continue to do so for a very long period of time. Fig. 135 illustrates the development of the centre lathe to an automatic lathe with respect to control of the linear movement of the cutting tool.

QUESTIONS ON CHAPTER SIX

Part A

1. Define the term "Machine Tool".
2. Give three advantages obtained when producing a surface on a machine tool as against producing a similar surface at the bench.
3. What is meant by generating?
4. What is meant by forming?
5. What are the essential geometric movements if a cylindrical surface is to be produced on a lathe? Illustrate your answer with a simple sketch.
6. Make a neat sketch showing a formed surface using a shaping machine.
7. Explain, with a sketch, how a plane surface is generated when facing the end of a bar on a centre lathe.
8. Make a neat sketch showing the method of guiding the saddle along the bed of a centre lathe.
9. Sketch the method of obtaining movement of the saddle of a centre lathe.
10. Why is the dovetail slide widely used in engineering?
11. What is meant by an indexing dial?
12. By means of simple diagrams illustrate how motion may be transmitted at 90°.
13. What is the purpose of a rack and pinion? Sketch a simple engineering application.
14. Give two advantages when using leather belts to transmit motion as compared with the use of gears.
15. Why would it be expensive to produce large numbers of components on centre lathes?
16. Give an example of a machine tool that produces engineering parts without actual removal of metal.

Part B

1. Make a neat sketch of a quadrant used to enable gear changes to be made on a centre lathe. What is meant by a tumbler gear?

2. Make a neat sketch showing the effect on a turned part in a centre lathe, if the path of the tool is not parallel with the lathe centre line in the horizontal plane.

3. A maintenance fitter called to replace a broken brass shear pin at the driving end of a lathe screw, replaces it with a steel pin. What would be the likely result?

4. A lead screw in a dovetail slide has a pitch of $1/10''$. If the divisions on the indexing dial are to represent linear movements of $1/1000''$, what must the diameter of the indexing dial be if the divisions are to be $50/1000''$ wide?

5. What is meant by backlash in a dovetail slide? What precautions must be taken when using the indexing dial in connection with backlash, when turning work in the lathe?

7 The Centre Lathe

THE centre lathe derives its name from the important fact that the line between the two "centres" of the lathe is a datum or "generating" line. We have seen, in the preceding chapter, the essential geometric conditions that are necessary if true cylinders are to be turned, and the requirements to produce conical or tapered surfaces and helices (screw threads). A centre lathe is essentially a practical application of the principles previously described. The requirements of a centre lathe are as follows:

   (i)   The work must be capable of being revolved about the centre line at a range of desirable spindle speeds.
   (ii) It must enable the work to be firmly held.
   (iii) The tool must be held rigidly and be capable of traversing parallel to the centre line of the lathe. Movement at 90° to the centre line is also required, together with the means of turning tapered work.
   (iv) Provision must exist for feeding the tool both into the work, and parallel to the work, and a range of differing rates of feed is essential.
   (v)   Provision must exist for determining accurately the linear movement of the tool per revolution of the work if screw threads are to be cut on the lathe.
   (vi) The requirements outlined above should result in a compact rigid structure, with adjustment for wear wherever possible, and providing the maximum safety to the operator.

It is also essential that the lathe be of sufficient size and rigidity to turn the work required and adequate horse-power should be available. This means that lathes are made in varying sizes and the student should be able to identify the size of a lathe. The main items are illustrated in fig. 136, and are as follows:

Height of Centres

This gives the distance between the centre line of the lathe and the bed, and is, in effect, the maximum radius of the work which can be accommodated on the lathe. Many lathes have a removable portion of the bed, which enables larger diameters to be turned. This is shown in dotted lines in the diagram, and such a lathe is known as a gap bed lathe. The maximum work diameter is sometimes referred to as the **swing** of a lathe.

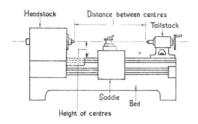

FIG. 136.—MAIN ELEMENTS OF A CENTRE LATHE.

Distance between Centres

This is the length of the longest bar that can be turned in the lathe, and is the distance between the live and dead centre when the tailstock is in its extreme outward position.

Surfacing

This describes whether the lathe is capable of turning work at 90° to the centre line.

Sliding

This describes the ability of the lathe tool to traverse, usually under automatic feed, a path parallel to the centre line of the lathe.

Screw Cutting

This means that provision has been made for cutting screw threads.

Hollow Spindle

A hollow spindle lathe offers many advantages, for it permits a long bar to be held with the minimum length projecting from the chuck.

Thus, a typical description of a centre lathe would be, 7 inch, 48" between centres, S.S., S.C., hollow spindle centre lathe. This describes a lathe whose centres are 7" above the bed, thus giving a 14" swing. It could take a job 4 ft. long and is capable of surfacing, sliding, and screw cutting. It is also a hollow spindle centre lathe capable of taking long bars. This is the lathe illustrated in fig. 136.

This lathe may now be separated into its main features, which are as follows.

Headstock

The purpose of the headstock is to support the spindle, and also to accommodate the necessary driving arrangements. Modern lathes have completely enclosed headstocks, but older type lathes have open headstocks, and reference to one of these will serve clearly to show their purpose.

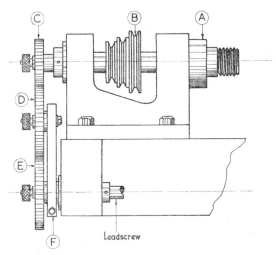

FIG. 137.—FUNCTIONAL DETAILS OF THE OPEN HEADSTOCK.

Such a headstock is illustrated in fig. 137. The spindle A is supported in bearings, usually phosphor bronze, with provision for the application of oil. The variation in speeds is obtained by changing the belt on the coned pulley B, which is keyed to the spindle. The spindle nose is threaded to take a 3-jaw or 4-jaw chuck whilst, at the rear of the spindle, provision is made for the interchanging of a driving gear. This gear meshes with an idler gear D and thus transfers motion to the driven gear E, which is keyed to and rotates the lead screw. These are, of course, spur gears, and the device used to enable different size gears to be accommodated is both simple and interesting. The component F is known as a quadrant, and can be rotated and locked at any position about the centre line of the lead screw. The idler gear D can be set anywhere along the axis of the slot in F. The procedure would be, having chosen the gears required, to set the idler so that it meshes with the gear assembled on the lead screw. The quadrant is now rotated so that the idler meshes with the driving gear C, and locked in this position. Fig. 138 shows the two stages in this operation. In this way motion is transmitted from the spindle to the lead screw, and accurate gears will allow the calculation of the linear movement of the tool for each revolution of the spindle. The modern lathe, however, will have an enclosed gear box, and different feeds or threads can be selected by the movement of external handles.

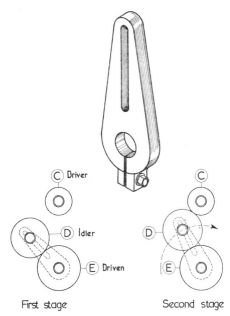

First stage   Second stage

FIG. 138.—LATHE QUADRANT.

The Tailstock

The tailstock of a lathe has a dual purpose. Firstly it is used to support work which is being turned between centres, and secondly it can be used to drill holes or centre bars using a centre drill. It is essential that the centre line of the tailstock be a continuation of the centre line of the lathe, at any position of the tailstock along the bed of the lathe, and, for this reason, the tailstock will be provided with its own guideway and bearing surfaces.

A typical tailstock is shown in fig. 139. Note the use of a Morse taper to locate the dead centre, and the nut and bolt to tighten the tailstock to the bed of the lathe. In order to feed a drill into the work it is necessary to provide a forward movement, and this is achieved by

using a square thread lead screw which transfers rotary motion of the
hand wheel to linear motion of the barrel. Careful study of the diagram
will show how anticlockwise rotation of the hand wheel will eject the
dead centre.

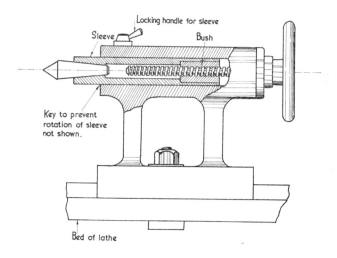

FIG. 139.—SCRAP SECTION THROUGH SIMPLE TAILSTOCK.

The Saddle

The purpose of the saddle is to support the cross slide, compound
slide and tool post, and also to accommodate the driving mechanism if
the lathe is fitted with automatic feed. As the name implies it fits
over the bed of the lathe and has its own guideway and bearing surfaces.
The accuracy of the movement of the saddle relative to the centre line
of the lathe is, as we have seen, of the greatest importance if accurate
work is to be produced. Many saddles are fitted with T slots which
permit castings to be clamped on them, thus extending the usefulness
of the lathe.

The Cross Slide

The purpose of this slide is to provide movement of the tool at
right angles to the centre line of the lathe and thus produce true cylinders.
A plane surface is generated in this way, and a simple and interesting
test is to machine say a 2″ diameter bar, taking a very fine surfacing cut.
If the flatness is now tested by the "engineers' blue" method, it is likely
that one or two faults will be detected. These are shown in fig. 140
together with the conditions that caused them. The design of the cross

slide is usually of the dovetail principle previously described, together with a lead screw and indexing dial.

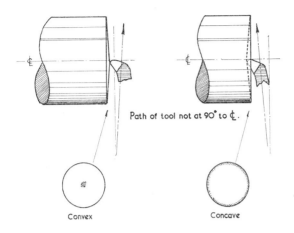

Path of tool not at 90° to ₵.

Convex   Concave

FIG. 140.—SIMPLE TEST FOR CROSS SLIDE OF LATHE.

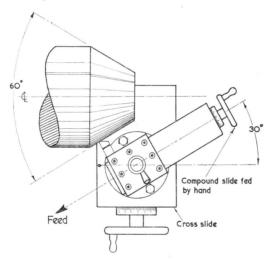

60°

30°

Compound slide fed by hand

Feed

Cross slide

FIG. 141.—COMPOUND SLIDE.

Compound Slide

The use of this slide permits movement of the tool at an angle to the centre line of the lathe, thus producing conical surfaces or tapers. It is similar in principle to the cross slide, but is capable of rotation about its centre line, and a graduated scale in degrees allows clamping at the desired angle. This angle, of course, must be one half the angle required on the component, and if the taper is given in inches per foot run, then a knowledge of trigonometry will be necessary to convert this into degrees. A simple set-up showing the compound slide is given in fig. 141. Note that the compound slide supports the tool post.

Tool Post

Lathe tools are held in a tool post, which sits on the compound slide. Tool posts may vary in design, but, in general, THREE main types are in use.

(i)   The single tool post is shown in fig. 142, and can only take one tool. Note that it can be rotated and clamped in any position; this is an advantage when small chamfers are required.

(ii) The four-way tool post is similar in principle to the single tool post, but it is now possible to hold 4 tools simultaneously, and this reduces the time taken in changing and setting tools. Once again the tool post may be rotated and clamped in any position, and a simple indexing device may be incorporated which will simplify the setting of the tool post at 90° to the centre line of the lathe. A four-way tool post is shown in fig. 143.

(iii) American type tool posts are suitable only for small lathes, fig. 144.

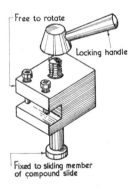

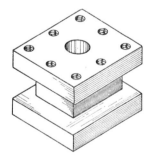

FIG. 142.—SINGLE TOOL POST.   FIG. 143.—FOUR-WAY TOOL POST.

The Lathe Bed

The purpose of the lathe bed is to support the headstock, saddle and tailstock, and also to ensure that the alignments of the moving saddle and tailstock are maintained. We have seen, in the previous chapter, how these alignments are governed by the use of guideways and bearing surfaces, and it is then essential that the lathe bed be of extremely rigid and robust structure, and not likely to deflect or bend under the cutting pressure. At the same time the guideways and bearing surfaces must be even wearing, and provision must be made for the lubrication of these faces. The life of the lathe, or its ability to maintain accuracy over a period of time, is considerably improved by preventing dust or grit getting on the bearing surfaces, and many lathes have simple protective pads to protect them.

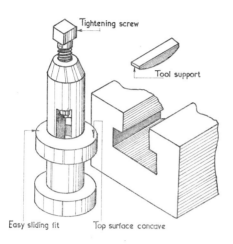

FIG. 144.—AMERICAN TYPE TOOL POST.

Work Holding

The method adopted for holding the work will depend largely on the type of job and the complexity of the turning. Cylindrical work or round bars are usually held in a three-jaw self-centring chuck, which utilises the three point principle previously mentioned. This chuck will, in effect, automatically bring the centre line of the bar coincident with the centre line of the lathe, and no skill is required from the operator. The principle is shown in fig. 145. Most 3-jaw chucks have a set of interchangeable jaws, which considerably extends the use of the chuck.

Fig. 146 shows some work holding applications of 3-jaw chucks, but it is essential to remember that a 3-jaw chuck soon loses its accuracy, and concentric work can only be produced if the machining is done in **One** setting. Should the job move, then it is virtually impossible to re-chuck it and regain the original setting.

K

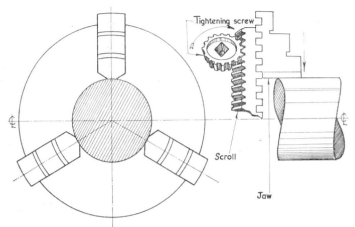

Tightening screw

Scroll

Jaw

Accuracy soon lost if black mild or irregular round bar used

FIG. 145.—THREE-JAW SELF CENTRING CHUCK.

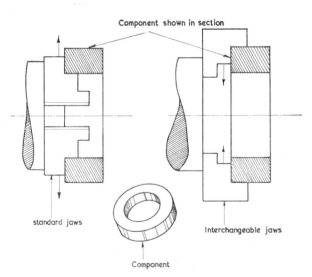

Component shown in section

standard jaws

Component

Interchangeable jaws

FIG. 146.—USE OF JAWS WHEN HOLDING LARGE DIAMETER
COMPONENTS.

Centres

The use of centres overcomes the limitation of a 3-jaw chuck in its inability to re-chuck a job accurately. Once again the centre line of the work is used as a datum, and this is achieved by drilling centres at both ends of the bar. Provided these centres are accurately drilled with a good finish, then the work can be removed from the lathe and replaced, yet still retain accuracy of location. This is of great value if the turned part is to be passed on for further machining, as the centres can be used for holding and locating the work during the following operation. Care must always be taken to ensure that the lathe centres which are inserted into the headstock and tailstock tapers are in first class condition and free from grit or dirt. This also applies to the mating tapers in the headstock and tailstock, as a true cylindrical surface will not be generated if damaged centres are used. Fig. 147 illustrates the principle and a typical application of the use of centres.

A lathe carrier will be required to transmit the necessary rotary motion to the work, making contact with a peg in the driving plate.

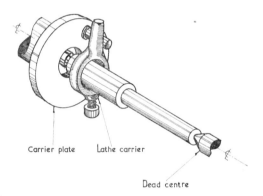

Carrier plate   Lathe carrier

Dead centre

FIG. 147.—TURNING BETWEEN CENTRES.

Steadies

Considerable forces may be involved when turning work on a lathe. In order to shear the metal, the shear stress of the metal must be exceeded, and during the turning operation a stress of about 100 tons/in.^{2} acts on the rotating work. If we consider the cutting or shearing action of a lathe tool, fig. 148, it will be seen that the torque or turning moment of the work, can be resolved into two components, or torque = force × radius ($f \times r$). This force F acts downwards on the tool and, provided the tool is rigidly supported, there will be an equal and opposite reaction on the work. In effect, then, the force shearing the metal is the equal and opposite reaction to the tangential force F, and this means that the work is subject to an upward force. A long bar of fairly small diameter machined between centres is certain to bend because of this upward thrust, and the principle is shown in fig. 148.

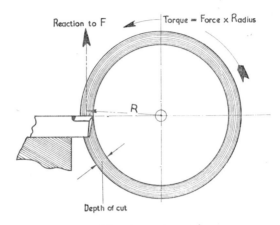

Reaction to F   Torque = Force × Radius

R

Depth of cut

View from tailstock

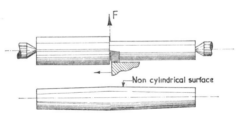

F

Non cylindrical surface

Front elevation

FIG. 148.—FORCES ACTING ON LATHE TOOL AND WORK.

The amount of bending or deflection, will be at a maximum at the centre of the work, and much less at the ends, where the work is supported by the centres. The machined bar would appear as shown in fig. 148, and would not be a true cylindrical surface.

The same condition exists if the end of a long bar is held in a 3-jaw chuck. Once again, due to the upward force acting on the work, together with the elasticity possessed by steel, the bar will deflect or rise and if the turner has set his index to take say, a 20 thou. cut, then much less than this will be removed, and confusion and error will result (fig. 149). To prevent bending of the work under these circumstances "steadies" must be used, the principle consisting in opposing the force causing the bending. Two types of steadies are in general use and their principles are shown in fig. 149.

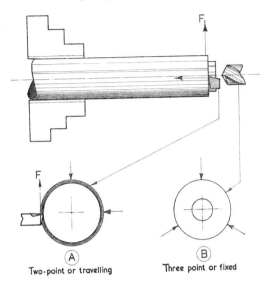

FIG. 149.—PRINCIPLE AND APPLICATION OF LATHE STEADIES.

Type A is called a travelling steady and is bolted to the saddle of the lathe. Thus it will travel with the tool, and is used when turning long bars between centres.

Type B is known as a fixed steady, and is bolted to the bed of the lathe. This type is suitable for supporting a long bar held in a chuck. Care is necessary when setting these steadies, and excessive pressure of the steady pads is not required. The work should rotate with reasonable ease when the steady pads have been adjusted and there should be no slackness between the pads and the surface of the work.

Tool Setting

The principle of maximum rigidity must be applied when the cutting tool is set in the lathe. It is the equal and opposite reaction to the force component in the torque of the work piece that shears the metal, and the greater the rigidity of the tool, the more positive and constant will be this reaction. A lathe tool with excessive overhang is an example of bad practice, or neglect of elementary machining principles, for it is very difficult, and sometimes impossible, to produce accurate, well-finished work under these conditions.

Fig. 150 illustrates the correct approach to tool setting. Note that the tool is on the centre line of the work with the minimum amount of overhang. The use of tool holders is not in accordance with the principle of maximum rigidity, and it is very unlikely that they would be used in a good machine shop. Their use can only be justified on the grounds of economy, as the tool bits can be used until they become too short but, even so, they are only suitable for small lathes and their use does not represent good turning practice.

If the amount of overhang (distance D in fig. 150) is excessive, then accurate work is difficult to achieve, due to the amount of "give", or movement in the direction of arrow A under the cutting force. Heavy cuts, if they do not break the tool, will set up vibration, and result in a condition known in the workshop as **chatter.** This will have a serious effect on the surface finish.

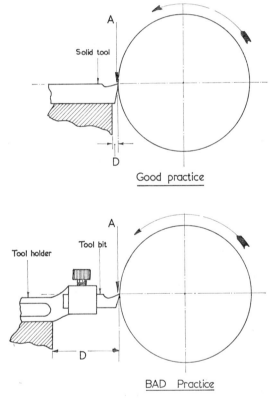

FIG. 150.—RIGIDITY OF LATHE TOOLS.

Packing pieces are usually inserted to bring the tool point to the centre line of the work, and there is no excuse for the use of old hack saw blades. A range of mild steel strips should be available in various thicknesses, and fig. 151 illustrates a simple geometric technique for setting the tool to centre. If the strip A is vertical then the tool point is truly central.

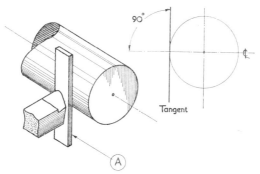

FIG. 151.—PRACTICAL METHOD OF LATHE TOOL SETTING FOR CENTRE.

Spindle Speeds and Feeds

Lathes, like all machine tools, are expensive, and they are only of value when they are actually producing work or removing metal. The rate, therefore, at which the metal is removed, will determine the output of the lathe, and it is a general rule that as much metal will be removed as possible, in the minimum time. Large metal removal, however, will involve greater forces and thus increase the possibility of deflection of the work, leading to inaccuracy and poor finish. For this reason it is customary to divide most machining into separate operations.

(i) Roughing.
(ii) Finishing.

The object of roughing is maximum metal removal in the minimum of time. It is usual to leave about ten to twenty thou. for the finishing operation. The finishing operation will involve bringing the work to the required limits of accuracy and to the specified quality of finish. The metal to be removed will now be small, as will the cutting forces, and the turner is able to concentrate his efforts on the final accuracy and finish of the part. This, of course, is similar to the principle adopted by the bench fitter, who uses a rough, and then a smooth file to bring the part to the required accuracy and finish.

The rate of metal removal will depend on,

  (i)   the metal being machined,
  (ii) revolutions of the work,
  (iii) linear movement or feed of the tool,
  (iv) depth of cut.

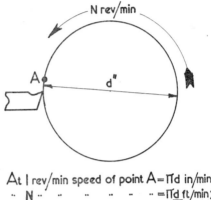

At 1 rev/min speed of point A = πd in/min.

   " N   "   "   "   "   "   " = $\frac{\pi d \text{ ft}}{12}$/min × N.

$$\text{Cutting speed} = \frac{\pi d.N}{12} \text{ ft/min.}$$

FIG. 152.—CUTTING SPEED OF ROTATING BAR.

All metals have an optimum cutting speed, which is given in feet per minute.

In the case of a bar revolving in the lathe, the surface speed will be the speed of the metal past the tool point and the principle and calculations are shown in fig. 152.

The cutting speed in feet per minute can be expressed as:

$$\text{C.S.} = \frac{\pi dN}{12}, \text{ from which it can be shown that } N = \frac{12 \text{ C.S.}}{\pi d}$$

Provided, then, that the cutting speed of a metal is known, it is not difficult to calculate the ideal revolutions per minute to turn the work, using the formula given above. Unfortunately, ideal conditions are seldom encountered when metal is removed on machine tools, and we have already stated that it is customary to separate a machining operation into roughing and finishing. A great deal of confusion exists because of this, and it is important for the student to appreciate that the ideal cutting speed is applicable only to the roughing operation where a large amount of metal will be removed.

Perhaps the following example, fig. 153, will serve to illustrate the principle involved. A 2″ diameter bar is to have a portion of its length turned down to 1¼″, and the finished diameter must be within plus or minus 2 thou. The bar is mild steel, with an ideal cutting speed of 60 ft. per minute. We see at once the difficulty of using our formula, for the

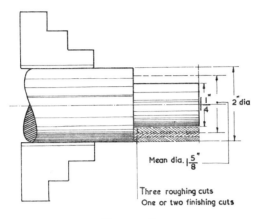

Mean dia. 1 5/8″

Three roughing cuts
One or two finishing cuts

FIG. 153.—TURNING TECHNIQUES.

diameter of the bar will reduce with each cut, and theoretically we should change the revolutions per minute after each cut. A more practical method is to select the middle diameter, which will be 1⅝″. The lathe revolutions will now be set, using 1⅝″ diameter, thus:

$$N = \frac{12 \text{ C.S.}}{\pi d}$$

$$= \frac{12 \times 60}{\frac{22}{7} \times \frac{13}{8}}$$

$$= \frac{12 \times 60 \times 7 \times 8}{22 \times 13} = \frac{20160}{143}$$

$$= 140 \text{ revs./min.}$$

The lathe is now set to run to the nearest speed to 140 revs./min., for it is unlikely that the exact figure will be available on the speed range of the lathe.

The problem now remaining, is to determine the linear movement or eed of the tool per revolution of the work. This is largely a matter of experience, but, in general, it will be about the maximum that the lathe can take, without overloading the motor or the driving arrangement. An average 7″ lathe will take a depth of cut of 1/10″ at a feed of 1/100″ per revolution with no undue strain.

Reverting back to the example in fig. 153, the total feed-in of the tool will be ⅜″, for ¾″ is to be removed. The following procedure will now be adopted, and the student is strongly advised to adopt this technique.

(i)   Chuck the work using a 3-jaw chuck, ensuring that it is running fairly true for, as previously mentioned, these chucks soon lose their accuracy.

(ii)   With the work stationary, feed in the tool so that it just touches the work.

(iii)   Set the indexing dial to zero, removing all backlash.

(iv)   Index the tool 0.1 inch into the work, and take a cut. If coolant is available, it should be applied in a steady stream. The feed should be approximately .010 inch per revolution.

(v)   At the end of the cut, disengage the automatic feed, stop the lathe, and return the saddle to the starting position.

(vi)   Clean the work and check the turned diameter. The reading on the micrometer should be 1.800 in.

(vii)   Repeat with another cut of 0.1 inch depth, and check the accuracy of the indexing dial against the last micrometer reading.

(viii) Repeat with another cut of 0.1 depth.

(ix)   0.075 inch now remains, and the final roughing cut should be 0.060 inch, leaving 0.015 inch for finishing.

This completes the roughing operation, and the skilled turner will use his micrometer only once, that is after the first cut, and thereafter he will rely entirely on the indexing dial during the roughing operation.

Finishing

By taking deep cuts and fairly coarse feeds the roughing operation is soon completed. 0.015 inch remains to be removed, and we are now concerned with bringing the component to within the limits with a good surface finish. As the amount of metal removal will now be small, the speed of the lathe can be increased, and the feed decreased, ensuring a good finish. It is generally permissible to double the speed, thus the lathe would now be set to run at approximately 280 revs./min., and the feed decreased about 1/3 or 0.003 inch per revolution.

A finishing tool should replace the roughing tool. Once again the tool is set to touch the work and the indexing dial set at zero. A small cut, say 0.003 inch will be taken, and the resulting diameter read off on a micrometer. Let us assume that 0.009 inch remain. Provided the turner has confidence in his indexing dial he will now index the tool 0.005 inch, and this will bring the work 0.001 inch under the top limit. It is not a good plan to come within, say, 0.002 inch of the final size, for only high quality lathes are capable of taking cuts of 0.002 inch. This is due to the number of moving parts in relation to the saddle guideways and the cutting tool.

Perhaps the following will convince the student of the dangers of coming too close to the final size. Let us assume that 0.002 inch remain to be machined. The tool is now indexed 0.001 inch, and a cut is taken. For some strange reason, no metal is removed and the perplexed operator indexes another 0.001 inch, and takes another cut. Should the lathe be in poor condition it is very likely that once again no metal will be removed. Yet again the tool is indexed another 0.001 inch, and a cut taken. This time metal is removed but, unfortunately, the work may now be reduced by the whole of the indexing, that is to say by 0.006 inch and the work will be undersize.

This is a very common fault when using centre lathes, and is due to the amount of play or movement between the tool point and the saddle guideways. It is better, therefore, to finish with a final cut of not less than 0.005 inch, unless the lathe is of high quality.

Machining Components Using a 3-Jaw Chuck

The part shown in fig. 154 is to be produced on a centre lathe, and the following remarks will give some indication of the procedure to be adopted. Firstly, the drawing should be studied with great care and for some time, so that the finished job can be visualised. This is what is meant by 'reading a drawing', and unless the student can see, in his mind's eye as it were, the finished component, then he is unable to read a drawing. This calls for considerable skill and experience, but should the student be puzzled, he should make simple free hand sketches, and thus produce a picture of the finished job. It is most unwise and uncraftsmanlike to proceed blindly with a turning job, without a picture of the finished job in mind, and it can be said that once the turner has 'read the drawing' and formed a correct picture of the finished component, then half his work is done.

The component shown in fig. 154 has a recess at one end, a drilled hole and external diameters, together with a tapered diameter. It is evident that, apart from the linear dimensions of the diameters and lengths, the important non-linear function of concentricity is involved; that is to say, the taper and diameters must be concentric with each other. The centre line of the lathe will, of course, be the datum that will control this concentricity, but it is vital that this centre line be constant for the whole operation. In other words, if the part is to be turned on a 3-jaw chuck then it must be done in **one setting**. Careful examination of the job will reveal that this is quite possible, and fig. 155 shows the set-up to be adopted.

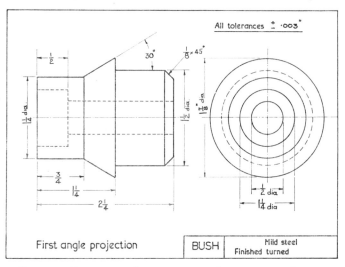

FIG. 154.—ENGINEERING COMPONENT TO BE PRODUCED ON A CENTRE LATHE.

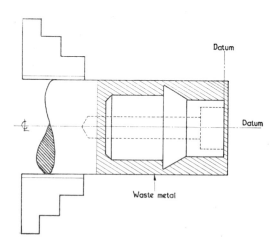

FIG. 155.—MACHINING BUSH IN ONE SETTING.

Note that we have reversed the job in order to bring the recess facing the tailstock. This will enable the recess to be machined at the same setting, and this means that the whole of the machining can be accomplished in **one** setting. The final operation will be to part off the work. The skilled turner, by virtue of his experience, will be able to plan his sequence of operations automatically, but it is not a bad plan if the young apprentice first commits his sequence of operations to paper. The following outline will give some idea of the correct approach.

1. Chuck job securely, holding on about $1''$ length and allowing $\frac{1}{2}''$ in excess of length of job.
2. Calculate, and set spindle speed.
3. Face end. This will provide the second datum.
4. Centre end using tailstock, and support with a running centre if possible. A dead centre may be used, and should be well greased.
5. With odd leg calipers, and lathe running, mark out $\frac{3}{4}''$, $1\frac{1}{4}''$ and $2\frac{1}{4}''$ lengths.
6. Rough down $1\frac{1}{4}''$ dia., to within about 20 thou. of line and finished diameter.
7. Rough down $1\frac{7}{8}''$ dia. Set compound slide to $15°$ and rough taper.
8. Rough down $1\frac{1}{2}''$ dia.
9. Remove tailstock centre, drill $\frac{1}{4}''$ dia. hole and open out $\frac{3}{8}''$ dia. Disengage feed shaft or lead screw. Spindle speed must be increased.
10. Using $\frac{1}{2}''$, $\frac{3}{4}''$ and $1''$ drills, drill counterbore just under $\frac{3}{4}''$ depth. Use index device on tailstock, or make pencil mark on sleeve. Reduce spindle speeds as drill diameters increase.
11. Finish recess with a recessing tool. Vernier calipers may be used to ascertain the diameter, using the indexing dial on the cross slide.
12. With a finishing tool, the spindle speed at double the roughing speed, and the feed reduced, finish off the outside diameters. The distances can be checked with a depth micrometer and an external micrometer.
13. With a parting off tool, feed in about $\frac{1}{4}''$ bringing the job to length. Set odd leg calipers to $\frac{1}{8}''$ and mark line for chamfer. Machine chamfer and complete parting off, fig. 156.

It is customary to remove all sharp edges on turned work, and a smooth file may be used for this purpose, or small chamfers can be machined with a suitable tool.

The sequence of operations described above is for guidance only, and illustrates the technique to be adopted. Several simple rules, however, emerge and they can be summarised as follows.

(i)   Study the job carefully and form a picture of it before commencing to machine.

(ii)   If possible machine it in one setting.

(iii)   Finish all roughing before starting the finishing operations.

(iv)   Always provide support at the tailstock end, where possible using a running centre.

(v)   Disengage feed shaft or lead screw when they are not required, for example when drilling with the tailstock.

(vi)   Change the spindle speeds to suit the operation being carried out.

(vii)   Break all sharp edges.

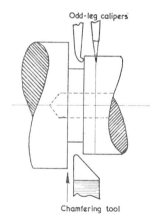

Fig. 156.—Machining 45°
Chamfer Before Parting Off.

Machining Components Between Centres

The component shown in fig. 157, may require case-hardening and then grinding to finish size. In these circumstances it would be turned between centres, the centres providing a positive datum. About 15 thou. should be left for grinding, so no finishing operations will be carried out at the lathe on the diameters that are to be ground.

The bar from which the component is to be made will be centred carefully at both ends, and this operation can be carried out using a 3-jaw chuck, and a centre drill at the tailstock. Centres are now inserted in the headstock and tailstock, and a carrier plate screwed on the spindle nose. When one half of the work has been turned, the work is reversed and the lathe carrier tightened on the opposite. Care should be taken not to damage the work with the tightening screw of the carrier.

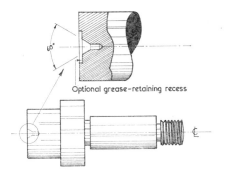

Optional grease-retaining recess

FIG. 157.—COMPONENT TURNED BETWEEN CENTRES.

Many lathes are fitted with an adjustable tailstock, which allows the turning of slow tapers, and this means that it is essential to measure along the bar with a micrometer after machining, to ensure that the work is not tapered due to an offset in the tailstock. A rapid and visual check of the tailstock is shown in fig. 158. Much the same technique will be adopted when turning between centres as when turning with the 3-jaw chuck. Although the method of holding the work may be different, the techniques of metal removal in order to produce a well finished accurate component in minimum time will be the same.

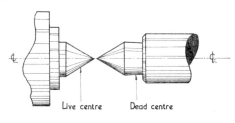

Live centre   Dead centre

Plan view

FIG. 158.—VISUAL CHECKING OF LATHE CENTRES.

Summary

There are, of course, many other operations that can be carried out on a centre lathe. These include boring, screw cutting, taper turning by offsetting the tailstock, together with the use of a 4-jaw chuck and face plate. The techniques, however, remain the same, if accurate well finished work is to be produced in reasonable time. Absolute rigidity is essential of both work and tool, and the correct tool should be chosen for the operation in hand. Most lathes have a wide range of spindle speeds and feeds, and the student should take full advantage of this, by changing the speeds and feeds as often as may be needed to suit the machining conditions.

There are also several safety precautions to be observed. The first essential is to be able to stop the lathe quickly, should anything go wrong. Before starting work on a strange lathe the student should make himself thoroughly familiar with the controls. Secondly, there is the danger of personal injury to the student, for the lathe is a power driven apparatus and capable of causing serious injury. The swarf produced by the lathe often possesses a razor-like edge, and should never be handled with bare hands. Thirdly, there is the care and appreciation of the lathe, its accessories and measuring instruments used. Micrometers and rules should never be left on the headstock or in the swarf pan. There is also no excuse for leaving spanners on the bed of a lathe whilst turning. The skilled turner will ensure that his lathe is free from all encumbrances, and there will be provision for the storage of all the accessories used. Equally important is the need to ensure that personal clothing such as the end of a neck tie or loose overall cuffs do not get in the way of any moving part.

Finally, the lathe will be cleaned down after the day's work, and this will include the cleaning of the accessories used. Regular and efficient maintenance of the lathe, in connection with oiling and greasing of moving parts, is essential if the lathe is to continue to produce parts accurately.

QUESTIONS ON CHAPTER SEVEN

Part A

1. What is meant by the 'swing' of a centre lathe?
2. What is the advantage of a gap bed lathe?
3. Make a neat sketch, to illustrate:
   (i)   a sliding cut,
   (ii) a surfacing cut.
4. What is the purpose of:
   (i)   a headstock,
   (ii) a tailstock,
   in connection with a centre lathe?
5. Show, by means of a simple diagram, how the dead centre is:
   (i)   located in the tailstock,
   (ii) ejected from the tailstock.
6. What is the main use of the cross slide on a centre lathe?
7. Illustrate one example of the use of the compound slide.
8. What precautions must be taken before taking a sliding cut using the compound slide?

9. What is the essential difference between a single and 4-way tool post?
10. Why is it sometimes necessary to insert packing beneath the tool?
11. Sketch two work-holding devices used on a centre lathe.
12. Why is it essential to complete the turning in one setting when using a 3-jaw chuck?
13. What precautions should be taken before turning a job between centres?
14. Why are steadies sometimes necessary when turning long bars on a centre lathe?
15. What is meant by the cutting speed of a metal? Of what value is this speed when machining metal?

Part B

1. What are the main principles which govern the choice of either a 3-jaw chuck or centres when deciding how a component is to be machined on a centre lathe?
2. Describe, briefly, the value of an indexing dial when turning work on a centre lathe.
3. Show, by means of a diagram, the forces causing the shear of metal, and explain why the work tends to deflect or bend when a heavy cut is taken.
4. Explain the principle of roughing and finishing on a centre lathe.
5. Why is it bad practice to keep the feed shaft or lead screw of a lathe engaged, when drilling a $\frac{3}{8}''$ diameter hole from the tailstock?

L

8 Single-Point Cutting Tools

WHILST the purpose of a machine tool is to produce a desired geometric surface, in most cases metal is removed in the process, and single-point cutting tools find a wide application on lathes, shaping and slotting machines. It is also possible to use single-point cutting tools on milling machines, and a boring bar is a good example of a single-point cutting tool used on a vertical milling machine. It is important that the principle or theory of metal removal be understood in connection with single-point cutting tools and, for this reason, it is a good plan to consider the cutting tool as a simple wedge. This was the method adopted in Chapter 5 when considering the action of a flat cold chisel in removing metal at the bench, and the principle also applies to single-point cutting tools used on machine tools.

Fig. 159 shows a single-point tool removing metal at 90° to the centre line of a lathe. It will be seen that the cutting or shearing action is similar in all respects to that of a flat cold chisel, except that the force setting up the shear plane across AB, is the equal and opposite of the force component present in the torque or turning moment of the work. The rake angle is shown as R and it is now necessary to provide a clearance angle C, for the work will be revolving at speed, and considerable energy would be lost as friction if no clearance angle were provided. In order to make a closer comparison with the action of a cold chisel, and to show clearly the wedge principle, fig. 160 is a pictorial representation with XY on a horizontal plane. The dotted lines show the similarity of the lathe tool to the cold chisel, and may be compared with fig. 110 in Chapter 5.

Note, that once again the energy required to shear the metal will be proportional to the shear plane along AB, and the length of this plane will again depend on the rake angle A. A small rake angle will increase the length of the shear plane whilst a large rake angle will decrease the length of the shear plane, and thus reduce the force necessary to shear the metal. These conditions are illustrated in fig. 161, and it can be seen that large rake angles tend to weaken the tool and, in general, that the rake angle chosen for any particular metal will be a compromise between the maximum angle possible and the strength of the tool.

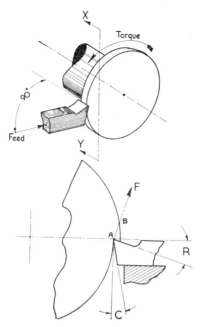

FIG. 159.—SURFACING CUT ON A
CENTRE LATHE.

The clearance angle also tends to weaken the tool and because of this it is customary to keep all clearance angles at a minimum. It is a common fault to grind excessive clearance angles; in general, all clearance angles used for external diameters should not exceed 10°.

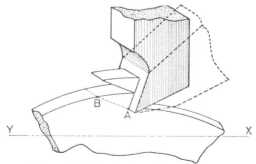

Outline of chisel point shown by dotted lines

FIG. 160.—SIMILARITY BETWEEN LATHE TOOL AND
COLD CHISEL.

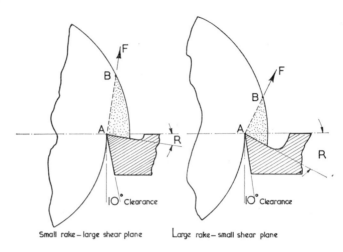

Small rake – large shear plane   Large rake – small shear plane

FIG. 161.—EFFECT OF RAKE ON SHEAR PLANE.

Orthogonal Cutting Tools

The tool illustrated in fig. 159 can be classified as an orthogonal cutting tool, that is to say the face of the tool is at 90° to the path or line of action of the tool. There is little doubt that this type of tool is the easiest to grind, and is often known as a knife edge tool when used on sliding cuts. Fig. 162 shows a plan view of a knife edge tool taking a sliding cut on a lathe. This tool is identical, with regard to the cutting action, to the tool shown and described in fig. 159, but in this case it is used for a sliding cut. If now a pictorial sketch is made of this tool,

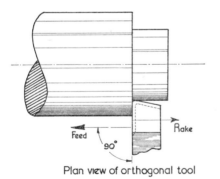

Plan view of orthogonal tool

FIG. 162.—ORTHOGONAL OR KNIFE
EDGE TOOL.

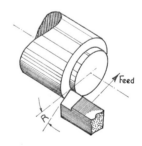

FIG. 163.—SURFACING CUT
WITH A KNIFE EDGE TOOL.

it can be seen that the principles of cutting or shearing remain the same, except that additional clearance angles are required, and fig. 163 shows a knife edge tool used for a surfacing cut. This knife edge principle is widely used in machining metal; for, as stated, such a tool is easily ground, and more important, easily sharpened.

Oblique Cutting Tools

When roughing down work on a machine tool, the primary object is maximum metal removal, and oblique, single-point tools are preferred. Perhaps it should be stated that the terms 'orthogonal' and 'oblique' refer rather to the principle of the cutting action than to the shape of the tool. The advantage of the oblique principle can be clearly seen by reference to fig. 164, which shows two bars receiving identical cuts. The depth of cut is the same in both cases, and so is the feed, but the force F which shears the metal acts on a larger area in the case of the oblique tool, thus the oblique tool will have a longer life. Alternatively, the oblique tool will remove more metal in the same life as an orthogonal tool; such tools are more commonly known as roughing tools.

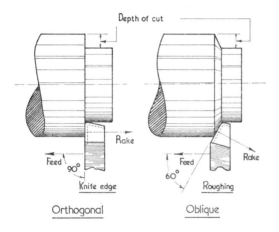

FIG. 164.—ORTHOGONAL AND OBLIQUE CUTTING ACTION.

Fig. 165 shows a pictorial view of the wedge action of an oblique tool, and it can be seen that the face of the tool is at an angle to the path or line of action of the tool. These tools are more difficult to grind and sharpen, as the effective rake angle is at 90° to the cutting edge. The correct choice of a single-point cutting tool is an important part of the turner's work, for there is a wide variety of shapes available, together with different lengths and cross sectional areas. We will find, however, that practically all lathe tools will be either orthogonal or oblique, and that the oblique tools will be used mainly for taking heavy cuts.

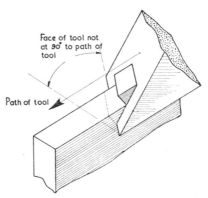

Face of tool not at 90° to path of tool

Path of tool

FIG. 165.—THE OBLIQUE ACTION.

Tool Shapes

Generally speaking, the shape of a single-point tool will depend on the type of machining operation to be carried out. With respect to lathe work, most of the machining will consist of either sliding or surfacing cuts, that is to say, parallel to, or at 90° to the centre line of the lathe.

The diagrams listed below illustrate the correct choice of a lathe tool in respect to the operation carried out.

Fig. 164. Straight Knife Edge and Straight Rougher (Both right hand)

The knife edge tool would be used for average reductions, whilst the roughing tool would be used for heavy cuts. Always used for sliding cuts.

Fig. 166. Straight Knife Edge Facing, and Straight Roughing Facing

These tools would be used for facing operations, the roughing tool preferred for heavy cuts, and would be classified as **left hand.** It is possible to use them for sliding cuts **towards** the tailstock, but this would not be considered good turning practice, as all machining should be carried out with the tool moving towards the headstock when taking sliding cuts.

Fig. 167. Straight Parting Off

This tool would be used to part off work, with the movement of the tool at 90° to the lathe centre line. Parting off is a difficult operation, and it is essential that the lathe be in good condition, and that the operation be carried out as close to the headstock as possible.

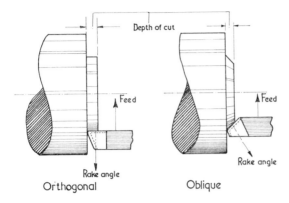

FIG. 166.—KNIFE EDGE AND ROUGHING SURFACING
TOOLS.

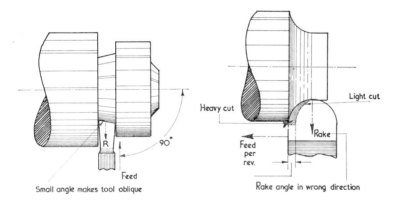

FIG. 167.—STRAIGHT PARTING   FIG. 168.—SLIDING CUT WITH ROUND-
OFF TOOL.   NOSE TOOL.

Straight Round-Nose

This tool deserves a short discussion. We have seen that in both orthogonal and oblique action single-point tools, the sloping face of the wedge provides the rake angle which determines the amount of shear plane and thus the energy required to shear the metal. The true rake angle is the angle of greatest slope, and it is essential that the tool moves along a path at 90° to this slope if the cutting action is to be orthogonal. In the case of the oblique action tool, the chip or sheared metal will move down the angle of greatest slope although the tool moves at an angle to this slope. This is shown in fig. 164.

If, now, a round-nose tool is used to take a sliding cut, the tool being ground as shown in fig. 168, then the rake angle, or path of greatest slope, is in the wrong direction, and a round-nose tool used in this way would have no rake angle, or a negative rake. The correct movement for such a tool should, evidently, be at 90° to the centre line of the lathe, and a correct use for such a tool would be to form the spherical surface shown in fig. 169.

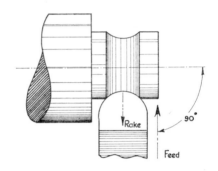

FIG. 169—FORMING WITH ROUND-NOSE TOOL.

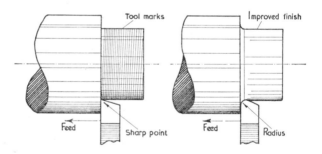

FIG. 170.—USE OF RADIUS TO IMPROVE SURFACE FINISH.

A round-nose tool, however, would be quite suitable for finishing cuts, where the metal removal is small, and fig. 168 shows how such a tool will tend to produce a good finish. Whilst the front part of the tool removes the full depth of cut, the centre portion of the tool removes very little metal and tends to clean up the surface. It has already been stressed that the cylindrical surfaces produced on a centre lathe are generated by a combination of work and tool movements, and the problem of obtaining a good finish consists in the removal, as far as possible, of the tool marks left by the movement of the tool. A sharply pointed tool cutting with a coarse feed, will produce a very poor finish indeed. If, however, a radius is ground on the tool point, then the finish will improve although the cutting action will be slightly less efficient if the radius is too large. The radius will also strengthen the tool point, as a sharp edge or point is easily damaged or broken. These principles are illustrated in fig. 170.

Straight Finishing Tools

The greater the radius on the tool, the better the finish on the work. As, theoretically, the curve produced by a radius of infinite size is equivalent to a straight line, this is precisely the shape of a finishing tool, and such a tool is illustrated in fig. 171. It will be seen that a straight portion of the tool is in contact with the work, and all tool marks will be removed as the tool takes a sliding cut. The cutting action is very similar to that of the flat scraper, described in Chapter 5, and once again a keen sharp edge is essential. The depth of cut must be small, no more than one or two thousandths of an inch, and a fine feed with low spindle speed is also essential.

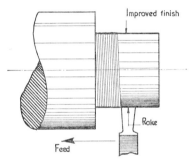

FIG. 171.—USE OF FINISHING TOOL.

It is evident, therefore, that the use of such a finishing tool will require a lathe of good quality, together with a high degree of confidence and skill on the part of the operator.

Bent or Cranked Tools

It should be clearly understood that a bent or cranked tool is merely a straight tool that has been bent in order to make the tool more serviceable, and to simplify grinding and sharpening. A simple illustration will serve to show the principle of bent or cranked tools. Fig. 172 illustrates a typical application of such a tool. Once again the arrow shows the direction of the rake angle.

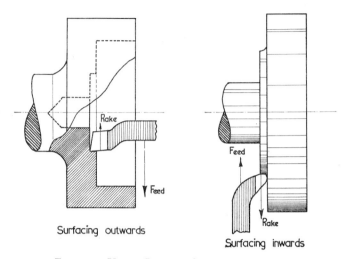

Surfacing outwards

Surfacing inwards

FIG. 172.—USE OF BENT OR CRANKED LATHE TOOLS.

Choice of Tools

The correct choice of a single-point cutting tool is largely a matter of experience and knowledge. Many factors are involved, such as the rake and clearance angles, the shape or form of the tool, together with the size or length, and the tool material itself. Generally speaking, a single-point cutting tool may be classified under the following headings.

Solid Tools

This means that the tool is, in effect, one piece and can be clamped directly in the tool post. The size of the tool will be given by its width, height and length, for example $\frac{1}{2}'' \times \frac{3}{4}'' \times 8''$ straight left hand, knife edge. Such a tool is shown in fig. 173 and it is very likely that the front edge of the tool is high speed steel, butt welded to a medium carbon steel shank. It is not often that lathe tools are made from high carbon steel, for we have seen that these steels will begin to lose their hardness at approximately 220° C., and at 350° C. the steel is relatively soft. These temperatures are easily reached when removing metal on a lathe, and as the purpose of a lathe is to produce cylindrical surfaces in the minimum of time, then heavy cuts involving considerable friction are essential if the lathe is to be used to the best advantage. This means that high speed steel is widely used as a cutting tool material, for high speed steel possesses a quality known as **red hardness**, or, in other words, it will retain its hardness even though the swarf or chip removed from the metal is at red heat. The use, therefore, of high speed steel single-point cutting tools allows the use of high spindle speeds and coarse feeds, but high speed steel is a very expensive metal, and considerable economy is obtained by butt welding a piece of high speed steel to a medium carbon steel shank. In this way the shank will be tough, whilst the cutting part of the tool will be hard.

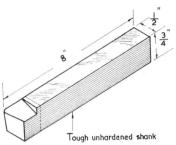

FIG. 173.—SOLID LATHE TOOL.

Tool Bits

Tool bits are available in a wide variety of sections and lengths. They are hardened, tempered and ground, and it is important to note that they are hardened for the whole of their length. All tool bits then are relatively brittle, and it is essential that they are used in conjunction with a holder. It is bad practice to insert a tool bit in a tool post without any sort of holding or support, and fig. 174 illustrates the possible effect of clamping a $\frac{1}{2}" \times \frac{1}{2}" \times 6"$ tool bit in a lathe tool post. Some tool bit holding devices are shown in fig. 175, but in general it can be said that the use of tool bits and holders can only be justified in terms of economy of tool material, for they do not provide the amount of rigidity possible with a solid tool.

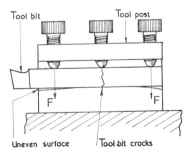

FIG. 174.—CAUSE OF TOOL BIT CRACKING.

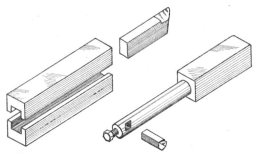

Fig. 175.—Application of Tool Bit Holders.

Tool Grinding and Sharpening

The grinding and sharpening of single-point cutting tools is, perhaps, one of the most misunderstood operations in the average workshop. One can be sure that the tools used in a capstan or automatic lathe would be sharpened or ground on a special machine operated by a skilled and experienced craftsman, and most firms engaged in the manufacture of aircraft will not permit the hand sharpening of twist drills. It is extremely difficult to sharpen a twist drill by hand so that the drill produces a hole to size, and oversize holes are usually the product of hand sharpening. When one considers the number of holes drilled in an aircraft to accommodate rivets, then it will be clear that because of the low margin of safety, it is essential that the holes be drilled as accurately as possible.

It should be clearly understood that the correct grinding and sharpening of single-point tools involves the use of special purpose grinding machines, equipped with adjustable tables, thus permitting the setting of the table to produce the required angle on the tool. The following remarks apply to the use of the pedestal grinder, and must be considered as a temporary expedient or an essentially practical method of single-point tool grinding, involving a considerable amount of experience and skill. It also is important to appreciate that grinding and sharpening a tool point are **two** separate and distinct operations.

Grinding a Single-Point Tool

The object of this operation is to give the tool the required angles. If we consider, as an example, a straight left hand knife edge tool, to be used for sliding cuts, fig. 176, then the following angles are required.

    (i)   Rake angle   (A)
    (ii)   Front clearance   (B)
    (iii) End clearance   (C)
    (iv)   Side clearance   (D)

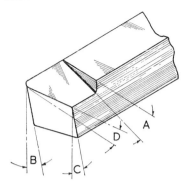

FIG. 176.—ANGLES TO BE GROUND
ON A KNIFE EDGE TOOL.

A double end pedestal grinding machine will be used, the purpose of the two working ends being to provide both a roughing and a finishing station. This complies with our much stated rule of roughing for maximum metal removal, and finishing in order to produce an accurate and well finished surface. We will find, then, that the pedestal grinder is equipped with two grinding wheels, one of rough texture and the other of smooth texture, or a coarse and fine wheel; the coarse wheel will be used for roughing down the angles required on the tool. Fig. 177 shows a typical double ended pedestal grinder, and it is usual to find the coarse wheel on the left hand side. Before starting to grind the tool it is necessary to ensure that the grinding wheels are truly round, and that the grinding faces are flat and parallel to the axis of the wheel. Several devices are available for "truing" a grinding wheel, and may include a mechanical wheel dresser, or a special type of abrasive stick.

Having "trued" or "dressed" the wheels, set the adjustable table as close to the wheel as possible (for both roughing and finishing wheels), and swivel the table to the rake angle required. The technique is shown in fig. 178, and it will be seen that a slight curvature must result on the cutting face of the tool, but this is of little consequence. The same method is adopted for the clearance angles, and the tool is then finished off on the fine wheel. The better the finish on the cutting face, or the angle of greatest slope, the longer will be the life of the tool.

In no circumstances should the tool be ground without eye protection, and if the machine is not fitted with a transparent guard then goggles **must** be worn. In order to promote even wearing of the wheel surface, it is a good plan to move the tool across the front of the wheel and not keep it in one fixed position.

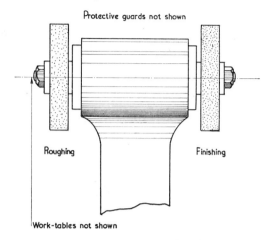

Protective guards not shown

Roughing

Finishing

Work-tables not shown

FIG. 177.—THE PEDESTAL GRINDER.

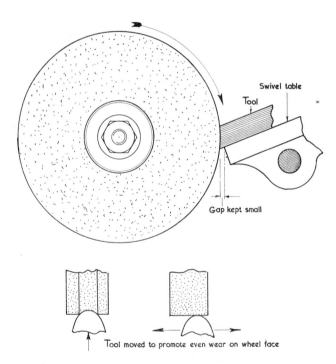

Swivel table

Tool

Gap kept small

Tool moved to promote even wear on wheel face

FIG. 178.—TOOL GRINDING TECHNIQUES.

There is one troublesome aspect in tool grinding on a pedestal grinder, and that is the problem of heating caused by friction. It is considered bad practice to quench high speed steel from an elevated temperature, because high speed steel is a poor conductor of heat, and minute surface cracks may appear on the tool leading to subsequent cracking. Despite this, many pedestal grinders are fitted with small containers for coolant, thus inviting the plunging in of the heated tool. It is difficult to state a hard and fast rule for circumstances such as this but, generally speaking, the best plan is to cool as often as possible or not at all. By continually plunging the tool into the coolant a severe temperature rise can be avoided. It would be bad practice to quench the tool after prolonged grinding.

Sharpening

After continual use the cutting face of the tool will tend to deteriorate, and this is caused by the friction of the chip or sheared metal as it moves up the angle of greatest slope. The whole object of sharpening is to restore this cutting face to its original smooth finish, and it is seldom necessary to retouch any of the clearance angles. This means that the sharpening of a single-point tool is a relatively simple and rapid process, and consists only of careful regrinding of the face, as shown in fig. 179. Care should be taken to ensure that the original angle is maintained, and the fine wheel would be used.

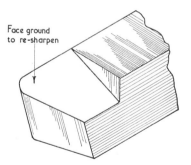

Face ground
to re-sharpen

Fig. 179.—Re-Sharpening a
Single-point Cutting Tool.

It is a most wasteful practice to regrind a tool to make it more suitable for a certain operation, say changing a tool to take a surfacing cut instead of a sliding cut. This would be unavoidable if only one tool were available but there is always a wide range of tool shapes suitable for many different operations, and the skilled turner will reduce the necessity for continual regrinding, with consequent wastage, by choosing the correct tool for the operation in hand.

In the event of a chipped or broken tool point, regrinding may be necessary, although much less metal will remain to be removed.

The Pedestal Grinder

Unlike most machine tools, the pedestal grinder possesses no geometric movements, having rotary motion of the grinding wheels only. There will, also, be no work holding devices, thus the tool to be sharpened must be moved by the operator's hand.

The peripheral or surface speed of the grinding wheel is extremely high, running into several thousand feet per minute, and a grinding wheel may be considered as a multi-point cutting tool. The abrasive material from which the wheel is made constitutes these points, and, due to the structure of the wheel, a very large number of points engage the work. The principle is very similar to the use of emery cloth or sand paper.

Great care, then, should be exercised when using the pedestal grinder to keep one's fingers well away from the grinding wheels, and it is vital that the gaps between the work-holding tables and the wheels be at a minimum. A wide gap may result in work being lodged or wedged between the wheel and the table, and it is possible that the grinding wheel may shatter, with centrifugal force hurling the broken pieces in all directions.

Wheel Changing

The grinding wheels should be changed when their diameters become too small to be of practical use. The cutting speed of the wheel is proportional to the diameter and small diameters decrease the cutting speed and reduce the efficiency of the grinding wheels. At the same time, it is customary to use only the front of the wheels and thus the radius ground on the work will increase, possibly beyond the desired value.

Wheel changing presents little difficulty, although there are a few simple precautions to observe. Because the wheels revolve towards the operator, or the cutting forces act downwards on the working table, it will invariably be found that the left hand nut securing the grinding wheel has a left hand thread. This is to ensure that the rotation of the spindle will not have the effect of unscrewing the nut, a condition which would apply if the thread were right handed. The right hand nut will, of course, have a right hand thread.

Before inserting a new wheel it is a good plan to test it by hanging it from a piece of stout string and lightly tapping with a small spanner or other metal object. A sound wheel will have a distinct "ring" and may be used with complete safety, but a faulty or cracked wheel will have a dead sound, and should be immediately broken up to prevent someone less informed using it.

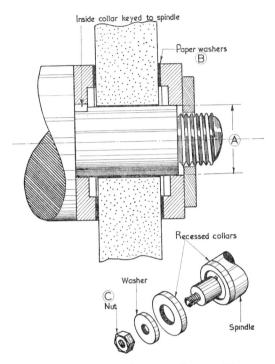

FIG. 180.—DETAILS OF PEDESTAL GRINDER WHEEL MOUNTING.

The usual method of joining grinding wheels to the spindle of a grinding machine is shown in fig. 180. The wheel should be a very easy fit over the spindle at diameter A, and must on no account be forced on if the fit is tight. This will inevitably lead to cracking of the wheel, and the serious possibility of disintegration when the wheel is put into use. It is usual to use thin paper washers, shown as B in fig. 180, and these should be replaced if the existing ones appear thin or damaged. Excessive tightening of the nut C is not required; reasonable pressure only should be used. The wheels should be "dressed" immediately they are assembled to the spindle, the work tables brought to within about 1/16" of the wheels, and the protective guards replaced. If, for some reason, the job has to be left at an incomplete stage, then the fuses should be removed to prevent the possibility of the machine being used.

M

Summary

Single-point cutting tools are widely used on machine tools in order to shear or remove metal. Because of the speed at which metal is removed, the correct rake angle is vital if the energy requirements, distortion and vibration are to be kept to a minimum. In general, **two** cutting actions are adopted, Orthogonal and Oblique, and the rake angle can be described as the angle of the slope down which the sheared metal or chip moves. The knife edge tool is a popular example of an orthogonal tool and presents little difficulty in grinding. It must be remembered that different metals require different rake angles, but clearance angles are always kept at a minimum.

The correct technique of tool sharpening involves only the restoration of the cutting face to its original condition, and several special purpose machines are available for this purpose, although excellent work is possible using the pedestal grinding machine, provided the operation is given the care and attention necessary. Solid tools are to be preferred for heavy cuts, but the use of tool bits and holders will reduce tool costs.

The following table gives the rake angle and cutting speed suitable for the more common metals used in the workshop, using a high speed steel tool.

Material	Applied Rake Angle	Cutting Speed Ft./Min.
Mild Steel	20°	60—90
Cast Steel	8°	40—60
Grey Cast Iron	0—10°	60—90
Brass	0°	150—250
Copper	35°	250—400
Aluminium	35°	250—400
Perspex	45°	350—500

QUESTIONS ON CHAPTER EIGHT

Part A

1. Make a neat sketch showing the forces involved when removing metal on a centre lathe.
2. Show how a turning tool shears metal.
3. Why are clearance angles necessary when using single-point tools on machine tools?
4. Why should clearance angles be kept to a minimum?
5. What is the importance of using the correct **rake** angle when turning with a single-point tool?

6. Sketch the principle involved when a cutting tool is classified as Orthogonal.

7. In which way does Oblique differ from Orthogonal cutting in respect to single-point cutting tools?

8. What is the essential difference between a roughing tool and a knife-edge tool?

9. What are the limitations of a round-nose tool?

10. Give the advantage to be gained by grinding a small radius on a knife-edge tool.

11. Sketch a finishing tool. What precautions should be taken when using this tool?

12. Make a neat sketch of the profile of a single-point tool you would use for:
    (i)   facing outwards,
    (ii) facing inwards.

13. What is the essential difference between grinding and sharpening a single-point tool?

14. How would you test a grinding wheel before using it to change a worn wheel on a pedestal grinding machine?

15. Why are most pedestal grinders equipped with two grinding wheels?

Part B

1. Make a neat sketch of part of a pedestal grinding machine spindle, showing clearly how the grinding wheel is joined to the spindle.

2. Describe, with the aid of sketches, how the angles ground on a single-point tool would be checked for accuracy.

3. Why is it necessary to regrind a single-point lathe tool after continual use?

4. Make a neat sketch showing how the work table of a tool grinding machine can be adjusted in order to grind a 20° rake angle on a single-point cutting tool.

5. What is meant by the term "red hardness" in connection with cutting tools?

9 The Drilling Machine

DRILLING holes is an essential process in engineering production, and there are very few engineering components that do not have holes drilled somewhere or other. Of all the metal removing operations that are carried out to produce a desired geometrical surface, there is little doubt that the production of an internal cylindrical surface is perhaps the most difficult. It is possible to produce a hole at the bench, using a cold chisel and a half round file, but this can only be done if the metal is relatively thin. To produce a hole $\frac{1}{2}''$ diameter in a $1''$ thick plate using hand tools is not possible, unless a drilling device of some kind is used.

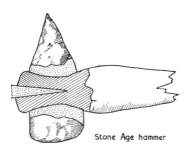

Stone Age hammer

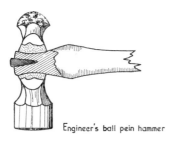

Engineer's ball pein hammer

FIG. 181.—ADAPTATION OF BELL-MOUTHED HOLES.

The necessity for drilled holes can be traced back to antiquity, particularly in the construction of weapons and tools, for the link between weapons, tools and engineering progress is a very close one, and a great deal of our engineering development and technique has resulted because of the demands for the tools of war and agriculture.

It may come as a surprise to learn that holes were being drilled by the Egyptians in 1200 B.C., over 3,000 years ago. The great advantage that metal possesses when used as tools and warlike weapons was already appreciated, but the problem remained, say of joining a copper spear head to a wooden shaft. It is essential that such a joint be permanent, and the best solution is to drill the haft of the spear, insert the wooden shaft and peg it in position. Much the same problem existed in the fitting of hammer and axe heads to their respective wooden handles, and there are many engineering apprentices at the present time who do not fully appreciate the principle involved. It will probably cause further astonishment to learn that the principle involved in the joining of a stone axe to a wooden handle was appreciated by the engineers of the Stone Age. Fig. 181 illustrates the method adopted.

It is not known how the holes were drilled in the stone, but one can assume that they were drilled from both ends, meeting at the middle. Such a method, using primitive equipment, would result in what engineers call a "bell mouth" hole, that is to say the hole would be oversize at its beginning. This is, of course, precisely what the Stone Age engineers required, for the insertion of a wedge prevents movement of the axe head in any direction. This simple device or technique has stood the test of many thousands of years, and is still used at the present time. There is, also, very little difference in the technique used by the Egyptians when drilling holes, and the technique used in modern workshops.

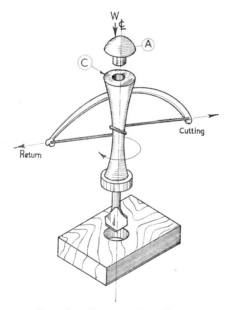

FIG. 182.—EGYPTIAN BOW DRILL.

Fig. 182 illustrates a simple bow drill, about 3,000 years old. The body of the drill could be wood, whilst the bit would undoubtedly be copper, probably heavily hammered to work harden it, and thus increase its hardness. Movement of the bow will cause the drill to revolve, and it is evident that the operator will press down on cap A during the cutting stroke. A downward force at W will also be required, and we can be sure that there will be liberal application of grease at C to reduce the loss of energy through friction. The action, of course, is not unlike filing, cutting taking place only on the forward stroke, the return stroke being non productive, consuming both energy and time.

This bow drill is evidently closely connected to the principle of the potter's wheel. The tool now revolves about its centre line, and a downward thrust is imparted to it. Provided then that the tool is designed to shear metal, a series of concentric circles will be produced, which will produce an internal cylindrical surface or hole.

Perhaps it can now be appreciated that a drill is a single-point cutting tool, and that rotary motion of the drill, together with a vertical feed, generates an internal cylindrical surface.

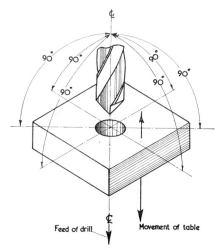

FIG. 183.—ESSENTIAL GEOMETRY OF A
DRILLING MACHINE.

Essential Geometry of a Drilling Machine

The geometric requirements of a drilling machine are relatively simple, namely that the centre line of the drill be at 90° to the plane of the work, and that the feed or movement of the drill maintains this accuracy. This is shown in fig. 183. The design of all drilling machines, therefore, will evolve around this geometric requirement and, as the drilling machine is a machine tool, we can outline the essential requirements as follows.

(i) The tool must be held.

(ii) The centre line of the tool must be at 90° in all planes to the surface of the machine table.

(iii) The tool must be revolved and fed vertically downwards.

(iv) Provision should exist for holding the work.

(v) A range of spindle speeds is essential, and the machine must be robust and rigid, with due regard for ease of operation and the safety of operator.

These conditions will apply irrespective of the type of drilling machine, for there are several different types in use, although the actual difference is mainly one of size or capacity.

The Sensitive Drilling Machine

We may regard the sensitive drilling machine as a modern version of the Egyptian bow drill. The improvements represent the effect of three thousand years of engineering progress, but essentially the basic principles remain unchanged.

Fig. 184 illustrates a typical sensitive drilling machine, which would be considered a bench type, for it is widely used in conjunction with bench work such as riveting and tapping.

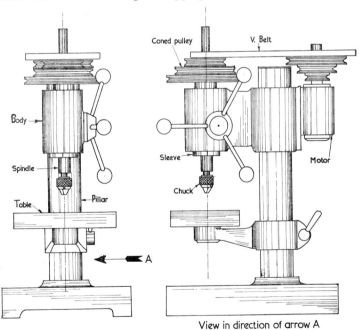

View in direction of arrow A

FIG. 184.—THE SENSITIVE DRILLING MACHINE.

Tool Holding and Feeding

The twist drill is the most common single-point tool used in the sensitive driller, but reamers, counter-bores and counter-sinking tools may also be used. The problem of tool holding in the sensitive driller can be divided into two separate parts. Firstly, the drill is to be joined to the chuck temporarily, that is for the drilling of a particular hole, and, secondly, the drill must have its centre as the axis of rotation. These are also the requirements of a round bar to be turned on a lathe, and therefore we will find that the sensitive driller is equipped with a **spindle**. The lower end of the spindle accommodates the work holding device, whilst the top end will have provision for speed changing and the transmission of torque or turning moment to the spindle.

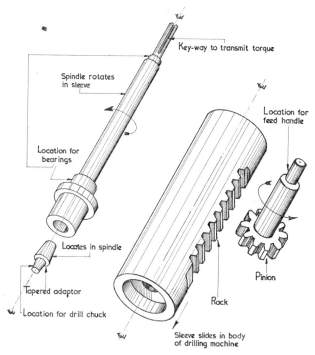

Key-way to transmit torque

Spindle rotates in sleeve

Location for feed handle

Location for bearings

Locates in spindle

Tapered adaptor

Location for drill chuck

Pinion

Rack

Sleeve slides in body of drilling machine

FIG. 185.—DETAILS OF DRILLING MACHINE SPINDLE AND SLEEVE.

A simple spindle is illustrated in fig. 185. Note the provision of a taper at the lower end. It is this taper which acts as the location for the tapered adaptor which, in turn, locates the self centring chuck. The spindle rotates within a sleeve, and roller bearings may be used at the bottom end, with a ball race at the top. A rack is milled on the side of the sleeve, and the action of a constrained pinion meshing with this rack provides vertical movement of the sleeve. This is shown in fig. 185, and the sensitive drilling machine can be considered as a structure built around this compact unit, providing drive for the spindle together with a work table for the work to be drilled; the centre line of the drill is at 90° to the table in all planes and at any position of the drill or table.

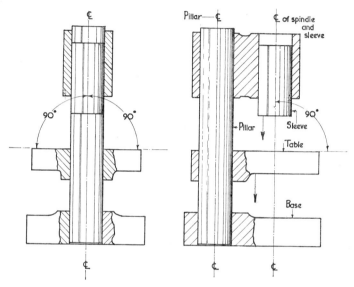

FIG. 186.—SLEEVE AND TABLE GEOMETRY.

A side view of a sensitive drilling machine is shown in fig. 186 together with the front elevation. The essential geometry is clearly indicated in both views, but there are very few sensitive drilling machines that will drill holes having their centres truly 90° to the surface of the work. If a drilled hole requires an alignment to within a few tenths of a thou. with respect to a plane surface, then it is highly improbable that a drilling machine will produce this kind of accuracy. However, for most workshop jobs they are quite adequate and, provided the machine is given the care and attention required by all machine tools, accurate well finished work can be produced by a drilling machine in the hands of a skilled operator.

Work Holding

The work table of the sensitive drilling machine is a plane surface or datum face, and acts as the locating face for the work to be drilled. It must, therefore, be kept clean and free from damage or swarf, for incorrect location will cause an alignment error of the drilled hole.

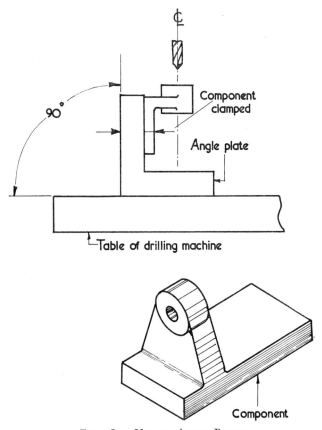

FIG. 187.—USE OF ANGLE PLATE.

There is provision on some sensitive drillers for tilting the table at an angle, and great care must be exercised in restoring the table to its true position. The holding of work by hand when drilling should be avoided and, wherever possible, the work should be held in a vice or clamped to the table. The use of an angle plate is essential for the type of drilling operation shown in fig. 187.

The drilling of large holes in thin plate can be a dangerous undertaking, and flat pieces of wood should be used as shown in fig. 188. It is quite possible for a drill to screw itself through the hole shown in fig. 188, and this will result in the work being revolved by the drill, with injury to the operator if he is holding the component by hand.

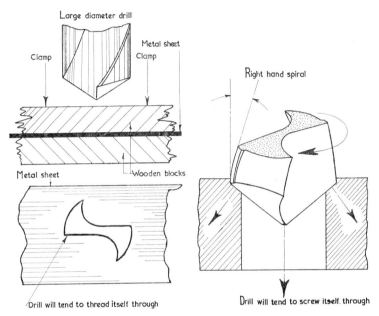

FIG. 188.—DRILLING THIN SHEET METAL WITH LARGE DIAMETER TWIST DRILL.

FIG. 189.—OPENING OUT LARGE DIAMETER HOLES.

The opening out of large holes, fig. 189, is also dangerous. If a small amount of metal remains on the diameter, the drill will tend to screw itself into the work, probably seize and revolve the work. This effect is due to the right hand spiral possessed by most drills, and for this reason reamers are provided with straight or left hand spirals.

Drilling Techniques

The purpose of a drilling machine, as we have seen, is to generate holes but, unlike a centre lathe, there are no indexing dials attached to a drilling machine. Provided due care is taken in ensuring that the set up is clean and rigid, the alignment of the holes drilled is outside the

control of the operator, and will depend on the geometric accuracy of
the drilling machine. The linear dimensions involved when drilling
holes will be the diameter of the hole drilled, and the distance from the
hole centre line to another hole centre line or datum face, together
perhaps with the depth of a drilled hole. These linear dimensions are
shown in fig. 190.

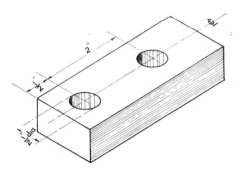

FIG. 190.—LINEAR DIMENSIONS WHEN DRILLING
HOLES.

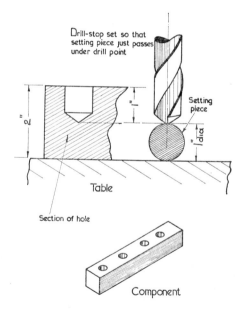

FIG. 191.—SETTING FOR DEPTH ON THE DRILLING
MACHINE.

This means that the drilling of holes to given centre distances or at given distances from datum faces, requires accurate marking out and centre punching. A great deal of skill and experience is required if accurate work is to be carried out. The diameter of the hole drilled will depend, largely, on the precision and accuracy to which the drill has been sharpened. With regard to the depth of the drilled hole, a measure of accuracy can be achieved, for most drilling machines are fitted with stops, and this allows fairly accurate setting of depth.

The procedure is shown in fig. 191, where four holes are required to a depth of 1″. The thickness of the work is 2″, and this can be checked with a micrometer. A setting piece can now be used, possibly a short length of 1″ dia. silver steel rod, and the stop is set so that the drill just makes contact with the setting piece.

This device should always be used when countersinking for rivets, chamfering large holes, or counterboring for socket screws.

Speeds and Feeds

The formula, cutting speed $= \dfrac{\pi dN}{12}$ may be used in order to calculate the approximate spindle speeds when drilling holes. In general the smaller the diameter of the drill used, the higher will be the spindle speed. It is seldom that the formula given above is used when drilling holes, and the best procedure is to rely on experience, or refer to the excellent tables supplied by most twist drill manufacturers. It will be evident that the use of the sensitive drilling machine is restricted to drills of small diameter, and a range of relatively high speeds will be provided, speed changes being effected by changing the belt position on the coned pulleys.

Thus the capacity of a sensitive drilling machine seldom exceeds $\frac{1}{4}$″ diameter, and the use of larger diameter drills will mean that the spindle speed will be much too high. This also applies to the use of counterboring and countersinking tools for, in addition to the large diameters of these tools, there is a large tool-work contact area, and any attempt to countersink using a sensitive drilling machine will inevitably lead to considerable vibration and "chatter". It is essential that these operations be carried out on a more robust type of drilling machine, equipped with a range of low speeds. A pillar drilling machine is usually employed for this purpose.

Feeding the Drill

The feeding of the drill in a sensitive drilling machine is motivated by hand, thus permitting a sense of touch or feel, essential when drilling small holes, and the name 'sensitive' driller is derived from this fact.

No hard and fast rule can be adopted with regard to the rate of feed. Much depends on the metal being drilled, the sharpness of the drill, the amount of coolant supplied, and the condition of the drilling machine used. Excessive pressure, if it does not break the drill, will almost certainly cause the drill to bend or deflect, causing an alignment error. In general, easy but firm pressure should be applied, care being taken to ease off this pressure as the drill breaks through, otherwise the drill will tend to "snatch" as it breaks through the lower surface of the work.

All drilling should be carried out with the sleeve carrying the spindle in its highest position. This means that the drilling table must be raised so that the surface of the work just clears the drill with the sleeve in its highest position. This principle promotes greater rigidity, essential for all machine tool operations. This principle is illustrated in fig. 192.

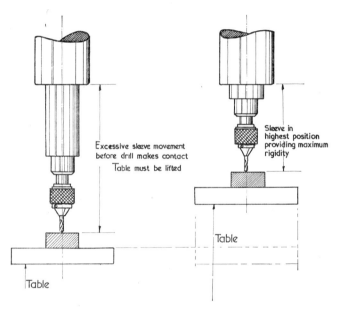

Excessive sleeve movement before drill makes contact
Table must be lifted

Sleeve in highest position providing maximum rigidity

Table

Table

FIG. 192.—CORRECT POSITION OF SLEEVE WHEN DRILLING.

Spade Drills

The twist drill is of relatively recent origin, and was introduced about 100 years ago. Prior to this, all drilling was carried out using spade drills, and this is the type of drill shown in the illustration of the Egyptian bow drill.

The manufacture of a simple spade drill would present little difficulty to a good practical engineer. Let us assume that a drilling machine is available, and he wishes to drill a $\frac{3}{8}''$ diameter hole in $\frac{1}{2}''$ thick mild steel bar. All he requires is a short piece of $\frac{1}{4}''$ diameter silver steel (high carbon steel), say about 4″ long, and provision for heating this steel to bright cherry red, together with the hand tools found in most small workshops. Within about one hour of beginning to make the spade drill, it should be possible to drill the hole in the steel bar. It is well worth while repeating this statement, for we are saying, in effect, that the drill can be made, and the hole drilled, all in the space of one hour. This is a very good example of the practical application of many of the techniques and processes described in this book, for there is little point in learning these techniques and then failing to apply them.

It has already been stated that engineers are concerned with making things, and it is important that the engineer possesses the knowledge or "know how". There is, of course, no substitute for actual practical experience, but the preceding chapters of this book have all been calculated to present this "know how" by basing them on the principles involved, or to put it in engineering parlance, on the "know why". We are now approaching the end of our First Year in the study of Workshop Processes, and perhaps the making of a spade drill will serve to illustrate the application of the techniques previously discussed.

Manufacture of a Spade Drill
Fig. 193(a) Heat end of a 4″ length of $\frac{1}{4}''$ diameter silver steel bright cherry, and forge as shown.
  (b) File ends to the profile shown.
  (c) File clearance angles as shown.
  (d) Harden and temper end.
      Drill hole using low speed and plentiful supply of coolant.

Note that the following processes are involved.
  (i) Forging end. This enables the use of $\frac{1}{4}''$ diameter rod and provides useful economy of material, together with a strong point and a rapid method of bringing the point to the approximate shape.
  (ii) File end to required profile. This involves metal removal at the bench, and accurate marking out if the drill is to cut to size.
  (iii) Harden and temper. This involves a heat treatment, that will give the point the hardness required, whilst the tempering operation will ensure that the drill will be tough enough to stand up to the shearing forces involved in cutting the metal.
  (iv) Drilling the hole. As the drill is made of high carbon steel, it will soften if the friction of the cutting action raises the

temperature of the cutting edges above 250° C. Thus adequate coolant must be supplied, and the spindle speed must be kept low.

To make, then, this simple spade drill will require a certain amount of knowledge of several workshop processes, and the ability of the spade drill to carry out its required task will depend on the skill of the operator in applying this essential knowledge. It can now be shown that, provided the theory of the shearing action is understood, a further improvement can be made, which will greatly increase the efficiency of this spade drill.

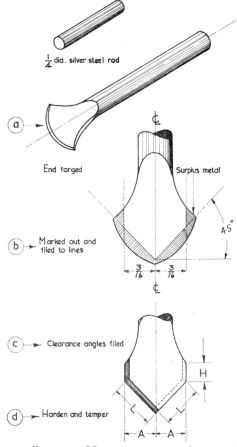

$\frac{1}{4}$ dia. silver steel rod

(a) → End forged

(b) → Marked out and filed to lines

Surplus metal

$\frac{3}{16}$ $\frac{3}{16}$ 45°

(c) → Clearance angles filed

(d) → Harden and temper

H

A   A

FIG. 193.—MANUFACTURE OF A SIMPLE
SPADE DRILL.

Reference to fig. 193(c), will show that the spade drill possesses no rake angle, or has a negative rake. If, prior to hardening, a small radius is filed or ground on the cutting faces of the drill, as shown in fig. 194, then the angle A will represent the rake angle, and the amount of energy required to drill the hole will be reduced for there will be a great improvement in the cutting action. A spade drill, made in this way, correctly hardened and tempered, and used with care, will have a remarkably long life, and it is not surprising that they have been replaced only within the last 100 years.

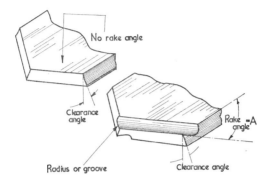

FIG. 194.—METHOD OF PROVIDING RAKE ANGLE ON
SPADE DRILL.

Defects of the Spade Drill

A spade drill will require sharpening when the cutting edges deteriorate, and continual sharpenings will change and eventually remove the groove forming the rake angle. There is only a small amount of bearing or grinding surface, shown as H in fig. 193(c) and thus the life of a spade drill will be short. If deep holes are to be drilled then the hole will fill with swarf or chips, and must be cleaned out from time to time. The accuracy of the diameter of the drilled hole is also difficult to achieve, for the drill will tend to rotate about its point, rather than its centre line, and a spade drill must have the conditions shown in fig. 193(c), if a $\frac{3}{8}''$ diameter hole is to be drilled.

Should the drill have the conditions shown in fig. 195, then the diameter of the hole drilled will be twice the large radius, and thus the hole will be oversize, for the drill will rotate about the point O, and the long cutting edge B will generate a circle of diameter 2R. Because of this, the drill will not have the same centre line as the spindle of the drilling machine and this will cause severe bending or undue strain on the drilling machine spindle.

N

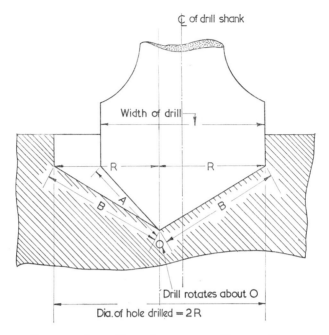

FIG. 195.—SPADE DRILL PRODUCING AN OVERSIZE HOLE.

It was, however, the introduction of high speed steel at the beginning of this century that ended the dominance of the spade drill. The advent of this new cutting material enabled high cutting speeds and feeds to be used, with no loss of hardness to the cutting point of the high speed steel tool point. We have seen that the spade drill is not suitable for this kind of work, and, ideally, we would require a drill that could be repeatedly sharpened without loss of the rake angle and bearing surfaces, together with the removal of the large amount of sheared metal or swarf that would be produced at the high speeds possible.

The Twist Drill

Essentially a twist drill can be considered as a twisted spade drill, and the principle is shown in fig. 196. It is difficult to twist a flat piece of metal as shown in fig. 196, retain cylindrical accuracy, and also provide a positive method of holding this twisted strip so that it will revolve about its centre line. For this reason twist drills are made from cylindrical steel bars, and the twist is produced by milling two flutes giving them a helical form. In order to reduce the friction on the bearing surface, a small land is left behind each cutting edge, and most twist drills have a slight taper towards their shanks.

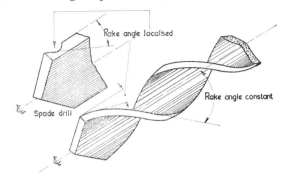

FIG. 196.—DEVELOPMENT OF THE TWIST DRILL.

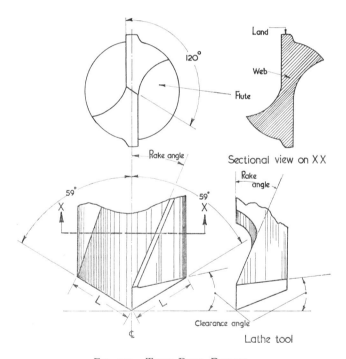

FIG. 197.—TWIST DRILL DETAILS.

Fig. 197 shows a typical twist drill together with a cross-section and end view. Note that the rake angle is equivalent to the helical angle of the flutes and a comparison is made to a lathe tool. The helical flutes not only provide a rake angle which will be unaffected by continual sharpening, but also provide a path for swarf exit, for the turning moment of the drill will tend to move the swarf up the flutes and thus out of the hole. The correct angles for sharpening a twist drill are also shown in fig. 197, and it is essential that the lengths of the cutting edges, and their angles, be identical from the centre line of the drill. Incorrect grinding or sharpening of a twist drill will produce the same effect as incorrect grinding of a spade drill, and oversize holes together with undue strain on the drilling machine spindle are the common products of hand sharpening. It must, therefore, be appreciated that hand sharpening of twist drills should be a temporary expedient only, and confined to drills of small diameter. Poor hand sharpening of say a 1″ diameter drill could result in serious damage to the bearings of a drilling machine spindle as well as very inaccurate holes.

Drill grinding machines are available, together with several ingenious devices for checking the concentricity of the cutting edges. It will be seen from fig. 197, that a twist drill has a relatively weak cross sectional area, and as the drill is hardened right through its section, it is not difficult to break the drill, so that care should always be exercised when drilling. The drill will also tend to bend or deflect, and when large holes are required to have precise alignment it is usual to bore them.

Twist Drill Sizes

Twist drills are usually available in three ranges, as shown below:

(i)   fractional,
(ii) letter,
(iii) number.

Fractional Drills

These are available in steps of 1/64″, from 1/64″ diameter to $1\frac{1}{4}$″ diameter as standard sizes. Sizes above $1\frac{1}{4}$″ diameter are also available but may be considered as special purpose drills, and would require a very robust drilling machine of the pillar or radial type. Generally speaking drills in excess of $\frac{1}{2}$″ diameter will be provided with taper shanks, and this taper provides accurate location. The torque or turning moment of the drill is not transmitted by the frictional contact of this taper, but by the tang at the top of the taper. This tang fits into a slot in the drilling machine spindle, and a drift must be used to eject the drill. Care should be taken to ensure that the ejected drill does not fall freely from the spindle as the cutting edge may be chipped when it strikes the table. Fig. 198 illustrates the taper shank drill and its removal from the spindle.

Letter Drills

Because a 1/64″ represents 0.0156″, or approximately fifteen thousandths of an inch, then it is evident that a fractional drill may not give the diameter required. This is likely when holes require to be drilled for tapping or reaming, and letter drills are available for purposes such as these. The largest letter drill is Z, with a diameter of 0.413″, and the drills reduce in size in steps of approximately $2\frac{1}{2}$ thou., to the smallest diameter letter drill A, which has a diameter of 0.234″.

Number Drills

The largest number drill is No. 1, with a diameter of 0.228″, which is 0.006″ below the smallest letter drill. The smallest number drill is No. 80 having a diameter of 0.0135″. All letter and number drills have parallel shanks as shown in fig. 198, and are used in conjunction with a self centring chuck, similar in principle to the three-jaw chuck used on a centre lathe. Fig. 198 also illustrates the principle of a drill chuck, for it is essential that the centre line of the drill be a continuation of the centre line of the drilling machine spindle.

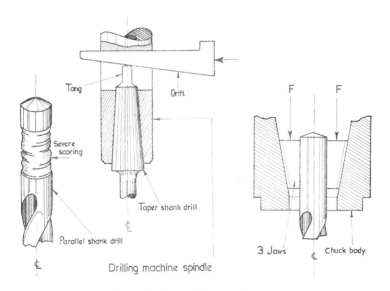

FIG. 198.—DRILL HOLDING DETAILS.

In accordance with an important principle, stated in the chapter on heat treatment, only the working part of a drill will be hardened. This means that the shanks of both parallel and taper shank drills are left soft, and they are, therefore, easily marked or damaged. It is essential, when using parallel shank drills, to ensure that the chuck has a firm grip, and the chuck key should be used for this purpose. A loose grip will result in severe scoring of the drill shank, with obliteration of the drill size, and the possibility of loss of accuracy when the drill is put to further use. The correct use of taper shank drills means that both the taper on the shank and the taper in the drilling machine spindle must be free from damage or swarf, and should be clean before mating.

Summary

Unlike the lathe, the range of operations possible on a drilling machine is relatively small, and consists of generating internal cylindrical surfaces. The geometric requirements also, are relatively simple, namely that the axis of the hole be at 90° to the surface of the work, although there are some instances when a hole may be required at a given angle. Despite all this, it is not easy to produce accurate work on a drilling machine, for the drills are of weak cross-section and very liable to "wander" if the vertical pressure is excessive. It is also difficult to produce a good finish with a twist drill, and the hole is often given a finishing operation by using a reamer.

The reaming of holes is also a difficult task, for there is a large tool-metal area contact, and the spindle speed must be reduced if vibration and chatter are to be avoided. Efficient reaming is seldom possible on a sensitive driller, for the speeds are too high, and a more robust drilling machine equipped with slower speeds should be used for reaming, as well as counterboring and countersinking. Correct use of the drill stop will enable accurate drilling to depth, and this is important when drilling the countersinks for rivets, if neat uniform rivet heads are to be obtained.

The drilling machine is a prolific source of injury, and the holding of work by hand should be avoided. The success of a drilling operation will depend to a large extent on the accuracy of the drill point, for of all the single-point tools used in engineering, there is little doubt that the twist drill is the most difficult to sharpen, and hand grinding should be confined to small diameter drills, and used only as a temporary expedient.

Spade drills are seldom used at the present time, but it should be remembered that over a period of three thousand years of use, they have only been replaced within the last hundred years, and it is well within the scope of a skilled practical engineer to make an efficient spade drill in a remarkably short space of time.

There is also another serious disadvantage when drilling holes. If the hole is to be drilled at a given position, then the centre line of the hole will have a linear dimension from a datum face, or from the centre line of another hole. These centres may be accurately marked out and then centre-punched in the usual manner, but the drilling of the hole removes the centre dot, and the centre line now becomes an imaginary datum. It is, therefore, impossible to find out whether the hole has been drilled in the correct position until after it has been drilled and, for this reason, the drilling of holes to accurate linear positions is a difficult matter. Several expedients are practised to overcome this problem; the hole centre may be 'boxed' or encircled, and a small diameter drill is allowed to drill a countersink formed by its point angle. The position of this countersink can be examined with regard to its position within the scribed circle or box. Should the countersink be off centre, then a small round nose chisel can be used to restore concentricity. A slightly larger diameter drill is then used, and the procedure repeated.

It is not until the operator is satisfied that the countersink made by the last drill used is centrally positioned, that the hole will be drilled

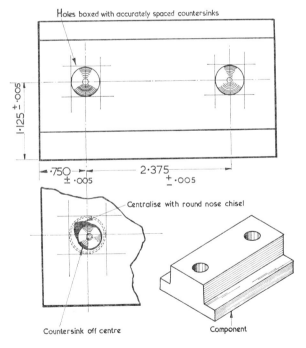

FIG. 199.—HOLE DRILLING TO ACCURATE CENTRES.

in the work. This technique is illustrated in fig. 199, and gives some indication of the skill and experience demanded if accurate work is to be produced using a drilling machine.

QUESTIONS ON CHAPTER NINE

Part A

1. What essential precaution must be taken when using a hand drill to drill a hole?

2. What is the main geometric alignment required on a drilling machine?

3. Make a simple sketch showing the essential features of a sensitive drilling machine.

4. Why is a sensitive drilling machine so called?

5. Why is a hand feed essential when drilling small diameter holes?

6. After drilling a $\frac{3}{8}''$ diameter hole through a steel bar, it was found to be out of true alignment. Give two possible causes for the alignment error.

7. What is meant by a spade drill?

8. Make a neat sketch of a spade drill used to drill a $\frac{1}{2}''$ diameter hole.

9. Show, by means of simple diagrams, why a spade drill will produce an oversize hole if not correctly ground.

10. Write down **two** limitations of a spade drill.

11. Show, by means of a sketch, how rake angle could be put on a spade drill.

12. Write down **two** advantages of twist drills over spade drills.

13. What principle is adopted to locate large diameter drills in the spindles of drilling machines?

14. How are such large drills removed from the spindle?

15. What is the principle adopted when holding parallel shank drills in a drill chuck?

Part B

1. Make a neat sketch of a drill point showing clearly:
   (i)   clearance angle,
   (ii) rake angle.

2. Why is it necessary to provide a small land behind the cutting edge of a twist drill?

3. Make a neat diagram showing the forces involved when shearing metal at a twist drill point.

4. What procedure would you adopt when drilling two $\frac{1}{2}''$ holes in a component, if their centres are to be within plus or minus ten thousandths of an inch?

5. Show, by means of a simple diagram, how rotary motion of the hand feed spindle provides linear motion to the drill.

10 The Shaping Machine

EXPERIENCE suggests that the shaping machine does not always receive the consideration it deserves in some engineering workshops. It is often considered as the hand maiden of the toolroom, for whilst a craftsman may rightly consider himself as a skilled turner, skilled shapers are extremely rare, for there exists a popular fallacy that anyone can produce work on a shaping machine, and little or no skill is required. There is no justification for such opinions, because the shaping machine is a machine tool, designed and constructed mainly to produce plane surfaces, and the correct use of this machine to produce accurate and well finished work calls for a very high degree of skill indeed. It is also a relatively simple machine to operate, for tool changing is easily carried out and the work is usually held in a machine vice.

It must be admitted then, that, it is not difficult to **operate** a shaping machine, but the use of a machine tool to best advantage involves a great deal more than just operating it for, as we have seen, the hall-mark of craftsmanship is the maximum use of the geometric movements inherent in the machine tool used. Perhaps the ease with which the work can be held, the tool set, and the machine operated, has instilled a sense of false skill, and has led to the practice of using a shaping machine solely to produce small plane surfaces of indifferent finish. We shall see, later in this chapter, the sort of work possible on a shaper, and it is hoped that the student will form a new opinion of the machining ability of the shaping machine, and accord it its rightful place in the engineering workshop.

Principles of the Shaping Machine

These have already been shown in Chapter 6, but it is worth while taking another look at the principles involved. These are shown in fig. 200. The plane surface is produced by "generating", which results from the path or line of action of the tool, and the line of action or feed of the work. A single-point cutting tool is used, and it should be evident that the tool shears the metal only on the forward or cutting stroke, and must then be returned to its starting point in order to take the next cutting stroke. This principle of a non-cutting return stroke is common to many of the processes carried out when removing metal at the bench, such as filing and hack sawing, but the shaping machine is a machine tool designed for rapid and efficient metal removal; therefore this non-cutting return stroke constitutes a serious shortcoming when considering the shaping machine for production purposes. Although most shapers are fitted with a quick return motion, which reduces the time taken to bring about the return stroke, the fact still remains that

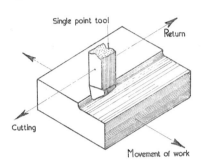

FIG. 200.—SHAPING ESSENTIALS.

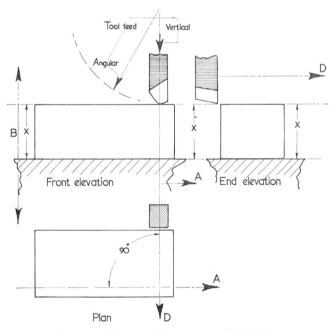

FIG. 201.—ESSENTIAL GEOMETRY OF SHAPING.

the return stroke is wasteful both of time and energy, and can be compared to the operation of revolving the Egyptian bow drill described in the previous chapter. Provided the shaping machine is to be used for the machining of a single component to a certain degree of accuracy with respect to both linear dimensions and non-linear functions, then it represents a tremendous advance over hand methods, or producing the part using hand tools at the bench, and this important fact more than outweighs the unproductive return stroke.

We may now consider the essential geometry of a shaping machine, that is to say the geometric relationship of the moving parts. These are shown in fig. 201. Note that Orthographic projection has been used, and a simple rectangular block has been chosen as a typical engineering component.

Front Elevation

Movement in the direction of arrow A represents the feed of the work, therefore a table must be provided and will evidently move on guideways. If parallel work is to be machined then the table must move in a truly horizontal plane, so that distance X remains constant. Provision must also be made to obtain movement of the table at a given feed, and movement is also required vertically in the direction of arrow B, so that work of varying sizes can be accommodated.

It is also necessary to feed the tool vertically downwards, not only to give the required depth of cut, but to machine work at 90° to the table, and it would be a great advantage if the tool could be set to move at any given angle to the table. This would permit the machining of angular work such as a dovetail slide.

End Elevation

Movement of the tool in direction of arrow D represents the path of the tool, and thus parallel work will only be produced if the tool maintains a constant distance from the table. This is shown as distance X.

Plan

The arrow D still shows the movement of the tool, and evidently the path of the tool must be at 90° to movement of the work, shown as arrow A in the front elevation. As previously stated, the angle 90° is widely used in engineering components, and this undoubtedly is the best angle at which to maintain the path of the tool in respect to the movement of the work.

A shaping machine thus possesses more geometric alignments than might have been imagined, and the correct use of these inherent geometric alignments is a considerable challenge to the users of a shaping machine.

Essential Features of a Shaping Machine

The Ram

The purpose of the ram of a shaping machine is identical to that of the saddle of a lathe, namely to provide accurate geometric motion of the tool. The principle adopted is that of the dovetail slide, with which we are already familiar. Fig. 202, shows in general detail the ram of a shaping machine and the dovetail principle will be clearly seen. The front of the ram is machined to take the head slide.

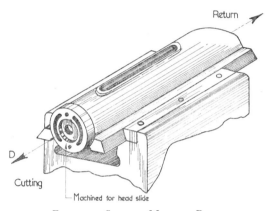

FIG. 202.—SHAPING MACHINE RAM.

Head Slide

This has two purposes, and they are as follows.

(i) To provide vertical or angular movement of the tool, together with linear control of the distance moved.

(ii) To hold or support the tool box.

This angular slide will be very similar to the compound slide on a centre lathe, for both have a similar function· and, once again, the dovetail principle is adopted. Linear motion of the slide is produced by rotation of the lead screw through the hand wheel, and an indexing dial will permit accurate linear movements. These are essential when a component has to be machined to a given size, and use of the indexing dial allows the operator to have control over the linear accuracy of the depth of the machined cuts.

In order to feed the tool at an angle to the surface of the table, the tool slide can be rotated within certain limits, and angular divisions on the circular part of the head slide permit setting at the required angle. This function, once again, is similar in all respects to the angular setting of the compound slide of a centre lathe, and perhaps the student may now appreciate the continual application of simple, but well proven, engineering principles. Fig. 203 shows a typical head slide for a shaping machine. Note how it is located and joined to the front end of the ram.

Reduced view of back plate

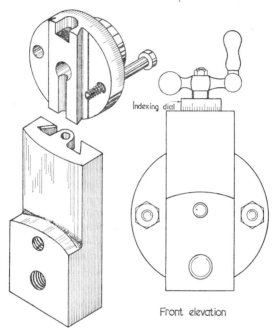

Indexing dial

Front elevation

Enlarged view of head slide

FIG. 203.—DETAILS OF SHAPING MACHINE HEAD SLIDE.

Tool Box

The tool holding device on a shaping machine is known as a tool box, and is an interesting example of how engineers solve the problems that continually occur in the design and manufacture of machine tools. We have seen that the action of a shaping machine ram is to and fro, or to put it in engineering terms the ram has a reciprocal motion. This is unlike the drilling or the turning of metal, where the cutting action is continuous, and reference to fig. 204 will show that on the return stroke there will be severe friction and wear on the tool point if the tool is rigidly supported; thus not only will the return stroke be non-productive, but it will also tend to shorten the life of the tool by dulling the point, and to prevent this undesirable state of affairs, a clapper box is fitted as part of the tool box. It is possible that the tool box may be referred to as a clapper box.

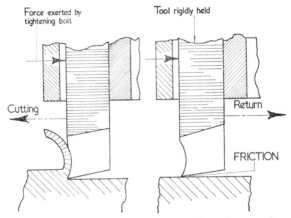

FIG. 204.—DISADVANTAGE OF A RIGIDLY HELD SHAPING TOOL.

The principle of the clapper box is shown in fig. 205. The tool holder pivots on pin A, and during the forward stroke the tool is rigidly held, the cutting force being taken up on the face XY. On the return stroke the tool holder is free to rotate on the pin A, and thus the tool point will rest lightly on the work during the return stroke. Note the method of holding the shaping tool in the holder. It will be evident that tool changing is a rapid and simple procedure, although the minimum length of tool should be allowed below the tool holder in order to ensure maximum rigidity.

Tilting of the Clapper Box

This is a further adjustment that can be made, and is carried out to reduce the frictional effects of the tool rubbing the work on the return stroke when shaping angular faces. It is not a simple principle that can readily be appreciated and provides another example of the neglected complexities of a shaping machine. Careful reference to fig. 206, will show the principle involved. Let us assume that a vertical cut is being taken as shown in fig. A. The axis of the **pivot** pin around which the clapper box rotates slightly on the return stroke is shown as XY. On the return stroke the tool will move along the arc shown as OP. This will not provide clearance for the tool point as it will still tend to be in rigid

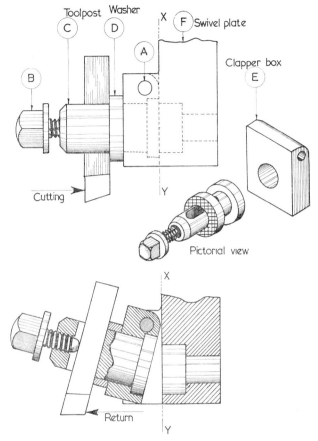

Sectional view of assembled clapper box

FIG. 205.—CLAPPER BOX DETAILS.

contact with the work, although capable of a slight upward movement.
The machined face will certainly be marked by the tool on the return
stroke and provision must be made so that the tool moves **away** from
the machined face on its return stroke. This is achieved by tilting the
axis of the pivot pin, as shown in fig. B. On the return stroke the tool,
on lifting from the work, will tend to move along an arc in the direction
of P, and thus move away from the machined surface. Alteratively if we
wish to machine the face shown in fig. 207, then the axis of the pivot pin
would be tilted as shown, thus allowing the tool point to clear the work
on the return stroke.

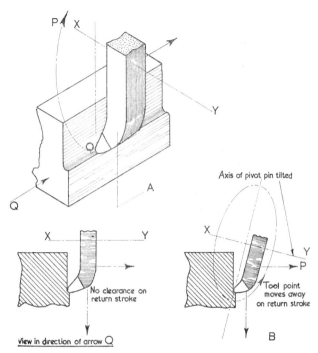

Fig. 206.—Clapper Box Tilt for Vertical Face.

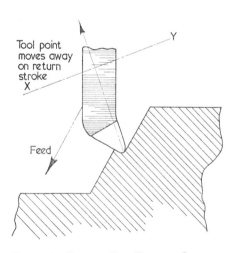

Fig. 207.—Clapper Box Tilt for Inclined
Face.

The tilting of the axis of the pivot pin is achieved by a small angular movement of the swivel plate. The principle is shown in fig. 208.

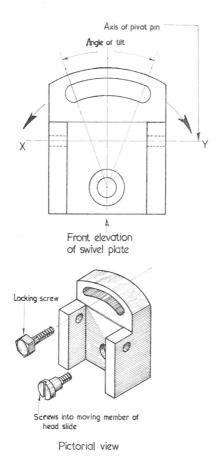

FIG. 208.—DETAILS OF SWIVEL PLATE.

Perhaps the student has now appreciated that the illustrations or diagrams used to show the application of the engineering principles now discussed have become a little more complicated, and require some engineering knowledge if they are to be understood. This is as it should be, for we are now approaching the end of our Course and we should, at this stage, be able to apply the knowledge gained.

o

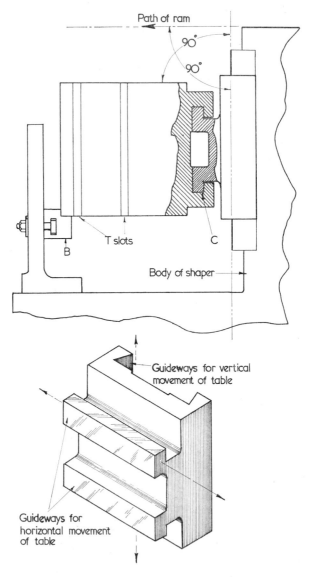

FIG. 209.—SHAPING MACHINE TABLE MOVEMENTS.

The Table

The table of a shaping machine is usually a box-like structure, but it is guided on principles similar to those used when guiding the saddle along the bed of a centre lathe. The method is shown in fig. 209, and it will be seen that this is not a particularly desirable arrangement. Although a principle similar to the dovetail slide is used, it is evident that the weight of the table, together with the weight of any clamping arrangement used, will tend to make the table sag or bend and this must result in work which is not parallel. For this reason most shapers are provided with a support at B, which must always be in close contact with the table. The portion C is also provided with guideways, which permit raising or lowering of the table, and yet maintain geometric accuracy. These guideways mate with the bearing surfaces which are part of the body of the shaper, and will be at 90° to the bearing surfaces which guide the ram.

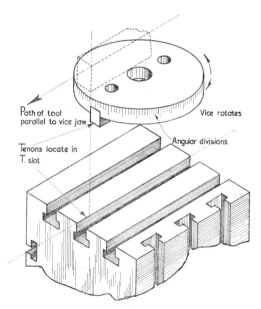

Path of tool
parallel to vice jaw

Vice rotates

Angular divisions

Tenons locate in
T. slot

FIG. 210.—PRINCIPLE OF SHAPER VICE LOCATION.

Work holding

A large machine vice is the accepted method of holding the work on the table of a shaping machine. The vice is bolted to the table, and the T slots are used to accommodate the bolt head which can be of rectangular

or square section. These T slots are also used for clamping castings to
the table, and it is also possible to clamp a casting to the side of the
table. For rapid and accurate location of the vice, the principle of
registers may be used, although perhaps the term 'tenons' may be more
familiar. The underside of the vice will have a slot milled, with two
registers or tenons as far apart as possible. These tenons must be
a good fit in the T slot of the table and, provided the tenons are in line
with the vice jaws, this is a good way of ensuring that the vice jaws are
in correct alignment. The principle or technique is shown in fig. 210.
The vices used on shaping machines are usually of the rotary type, that
is to say they can be set at an angle and tightened in this position. This
is a useful device, and allows the component to have its angular surface
machined as shown in fig. 211, which represents a plan view of the
operation.

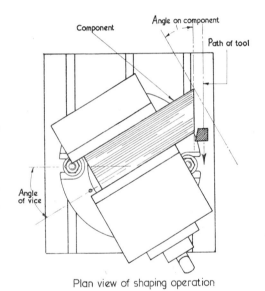

Plan view of shaping operation

FIG. 211.—INDEXING OF SHAPER VICE.

Functional Details of the Shaper

Most shapers are fitted with a quick return motion which reduces the
time of the return stroke but not the energy requirements. It is
essential, in the design and construction of machine tools, to make sure
that there are no moving parts outside the machine which could be a

source of injury to the operator, and, for this reason, most of the mechanisms which activate the movements necessary for all machine tools are generally enclosed out of harm's way within the body or structure of the machine tool. This, of course, is very necessary because of the inherent danger present in all moving parts, especially so when there may be a **six** horse power motor providing the initial energy, but it gives little opportunity for the student technician or engineer to observe how these mechanisms actually operate.

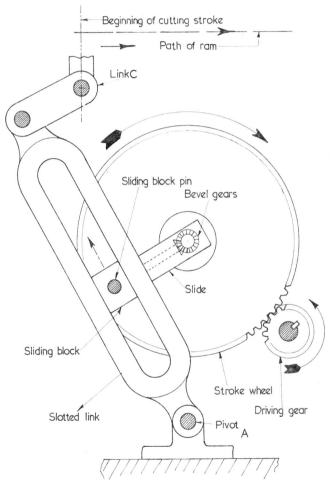

FIG. 212.—MECHANISM OF THE QUICK RETURN SHAPING ACTION.

The student is advised, should the opportunity present itself, to take every advantage offered in studying the mechanism that operates the moving parts of machine tools, and an occasional visit to the maintenance department where machine tools are stripped down for repair or over-haul would be well worth while.

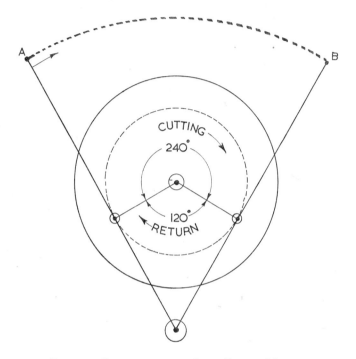

FIG. 213.—PRINCIPLE OF THE QUICK RETURN MOTION.

Movement of the Ram

The ram of the shaping machine will have linear motion, and a line diagram showing the method adopted is given in fig. 212.

The slotted link pivots at A, and the sliding block is constrained within the slot but is free to move up or down within this slot. The stroke wheel is, in effect, a heavy spur gear, and meshes with a smaller gear which is driven, through a gear box, by an electric motor. Thus the energy to rotate the stroke wheel is received from the electric motor, and rotation of the stroke wheel will cause the sliding block to oscillate up and down the slot in the slotted link and thus impart reciprocating motion to the slotted link. There is a small connecting link at the top of the slotted link, which is joined to the ram, and in this way the ram will move to and fro along its guideways. Fig. 212 shows the ram at its extreme left hand position.

In order to appreciate that the ram has a quick return cutting action, a simple diagram is shown in fig. 213. Point A represents the top of the link at the beginning of the cutting stroke, and as the stroke wheel revolves the link top will describe an arc. Point B represents the finish of the stroke. We see at once the need for the small link C in fig. 212 for, if the top of the slotted link were joined directly to the ram, then the slotted link would try to move the ram along an **arc**. The small link C will allow linear motion or movement of the ram along a straight line.

As the cutting stroke ends at B, then the stroke wheel will have moved through an angle of say 240°, but the return stroke will take place whilst the stroke wheel revolves through 120°, for there are 360° in a full circle. Thus the ram moves back twice as fast as it moves forward, so that the unproductive return stroke has been reduced by one half.

The student is advised to study this principle carefully, for it shows in a clear manner the necessary connection between technology and mathematics. Fig. 212 shows an essentially practical application of the theory shown in fig. 213.

Two other problems remain. A ram with a fixed length of stroke would be of little use, and most wasteful of time and energy if a small component requires to be shaped. This condition is shown in fig. 214. Evidently, provision must exist for adjusting the length of the stroke to suit the length of machined surface. Again the shape of the job may be as shown in fig. 215, and it is now necessary to be able to position the ram. The methods adopted are outlined below.

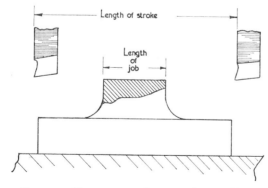

FIG. 214.—NECESSITY FOR CHANGING STROKE LENGTH.

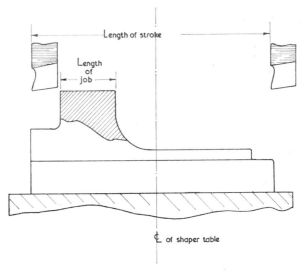

FIG. 215.—NECESSITY FOR CHANGING POSITION OF RAM.

Adjusting the Stroke

This is achieved with the aid of a small slide attached centrally on the stroke wheel. Rotation of the bevel gear A will rotate the bevel gear B and thus rotate the lead screw C. This lead screw operates the sliding member of a dovetail slide, and therefore the sliding block **pin** can be brought inwards or outwards with regard to the centre of the stroke wheel. The closer the pin is brought to the centre of the stroke wheel, the smaller will be the stroke, and when the pin is at its maximum distance, then the shaping machine ram will be on its maximum stroke. Fig. 216 illustrates further the principle involved.

It is possibly at this point that the student may have some trouble in following the principles involved, but engineers have always faced trouble of some kind or another, and the progress of engineering usually stems from a careful and painstaking examination of the problem, and then its ultimate solution.

Any method that will assist in the solution of the problem will be adopted; for example when designing a new type of aircraft it is quite possible that a complete section, say of fuselage or wing, will be constructed from wood, cardboard, or paper, exactly to scale, so that a complete picture can be had of the completed section, allowing measurements of length, space and volume. If then, the student has difficulty in following some of the principles and techniques outlined in this book,

he is strongly advised to adopt a similar procedure, and make it his
business to examine these details for himself at first hand.

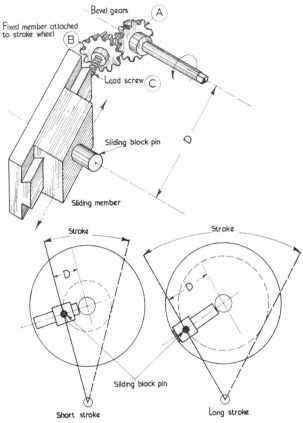

FIG. 216.—DETAILS OF LENGTH OF STROKE ADJUSTMENT.

Positioning the Ram

The positioning of the ram is a relatively simple affair and the
method is shown in fig. 217. Slackening of the handle nut at A, will
allow the ram to be pushed to the desired position; the handle nut must
then be re-tightened.

Feeding the Table

The movement of the table is essential if a plane surface is to be
generated on a shaping machine, and an automatic, or mechanised,
action must be provided if the operator is to be freed from the laborious

and tedious method of hand feeding. The device used is both interesting and ingenious for it enables not only the automatic movement of the table, but also provides a range of movements or feeds. The method is shown in fig. 218. Rotation of the stroke wheel rotates the slotted wheel shown at A, and this carries an adjustable arm, the eccentricity of which will be proportional to the distance of the **pivot** B from the centre.

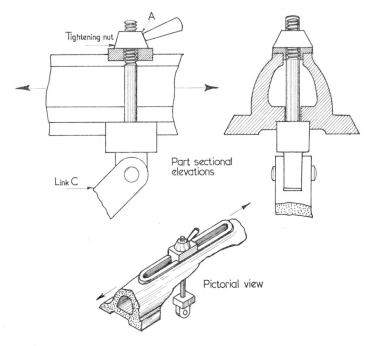

FIG. 217.—DETAILS OF RAM POSITION ADJUSTMENT.

This eccentricity will impart an oscillating motion to the link and will cause the lever C to oscillate about its pivot D. This lever has a spring loaded plunger E and the position of this plunger with respect to the slot F, will determine whether the feed is left or right handed. The feed may be increased by increasing the distance of the pivot B from the centre of the slotted wheel A, and this is easily carried out. The plunger E will rotate the ratchet wheel G, and as this wheel is connected to the lead screw of the shaping machine table, the table will be fed along its guide-ways.

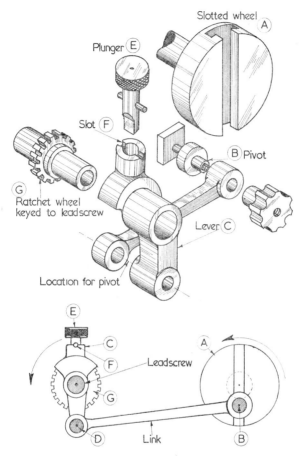

Slotted wheel (A)

Plunger (E)

Slot (F)

(B) Pivot

(G) Ratchet wheel keyed to leadscrew

Lever (C)

Location for pivot

E

C

A

F — Leadscrew

G

D   Link   B

FIG. 218.—DETAILS OF FEEDING MECHANISM.

Shaping Techniques

We have seen that the shaping machine possesses several ingenious mechanical devices and is a good example of how engineers apply simple mechanical principles to achieve the essential geometry and movements inherent in all machine tools.

Because of the ease with which the tool and work can be held, there is a tendency, as has been pointed out, to regard the shaping machine as a suitable method of producing small plane surfaces. There is no justification for this attitude, for the cost of a good shaping machine will differ little from the cost of a good lathe, and if the operator is to use the shaping machine to best advantage, then full use must be made of the geometric accuracy built into the machine.

The following examples will serve to illustrate the correct approach to shaping technique, and we will consider first the machining of the V slot in the component shown in fig. 219. We may assume that the slot has been marked out and the hole drilled, and all that remains is to machine the V.

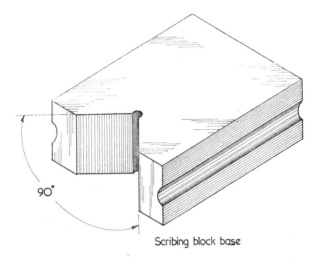

Scribing block base

FIG. 219.—COMPONENT WITH 90° V.

Shaping a 90° V Slot

We have already stressed the necessity for a close study of the drawing before starting to machine a job. It is a mistake to assume that a job is to be machined in the same elevation or portrayal of the work in the drawing. At first glance, the student may be tempted to machine as shown in fig. 220. This would involve **two** settings of the sliding head, and the use of two different tools.

The fact that we must make two settings of the head will increase our chance of error, for it is a basic rule when machining that, as far as possible, the work should be machined in **one** setting. If now we re-draw the component as shown in fig. 221, then it is possible to machine this V slot in one setting and with one tool, for the angle is 90° and provision exists in the movement of the shaper table that will allow us to machine at 90° to the vertical path of the tool. This means that one setting only is required and that one tool can be used; the accuracy of the 90° angle required will depend mainly on our skill in determining whether the

vertical feed of the tool is truly 90° to the surface table. Because the
sliding head is capable of being adjusted at an angle to the table, we must
first ensure that it is set in the correct position. This can be ascertained
by seeing that the indexing lines are at 90°, but a better method is to
check the vertical path of the tool, using a try-square and feelers, or,
better still, a dial indicator and accurate try-square. The technique is
shown in fig. 222.

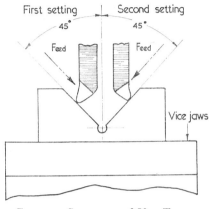

FIG. 220.—SHAPING A 90° V IN TWO
SETTINGS.

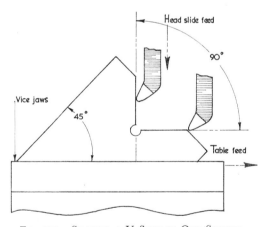

FIG. 221.—SHAPING A V SLOT IN ONE SETTING.

Having established that the vertical feed is truly 90°—and adjusted it,
if it is not—then vertical movement of the table will produce an angle of
90°, and the accuracy of the angle will be the geometric accuracy of the

machine tool. It only remains now to set the work at 45°, or with the scribed lines in a vertical position. A try-square may be used, or the popular "stick pin", which consists of a sharp pointed pin attached to the shaping tool. Chewing gum is ideal for this purpose, although soft clay can be used. The job is set so that downward feed of the tool keeps the pointed pin on the scribed line. The technique is shown in fig. 223.

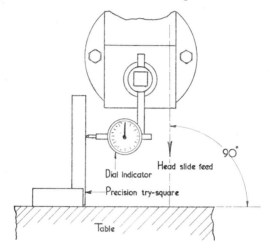

FIG. 222.—TESTING HEAD SLIDE FOR VERTICAL FEED.

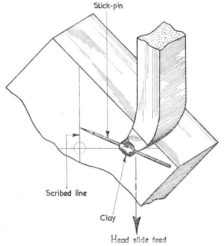

FIG. 223.—USE OF STICK PIN.

The V slot may now be machined, the feed can be automatic with horizontal movement of the table, and the depths of cut set by hand at the sliding head. These cuts are shown in fig. 224, and it is a good plan to rough out within about 15 thou. of the line, change the roughing tool for a finishing tool and complete the operation, with reduced feed and depths of cut. The accuracy of the angle produced in this way will be very good indeed and, in the event of an Inspector not being satisfied with this accuracy, then there is only one alternative, and that is to purchase a better quality shaper!

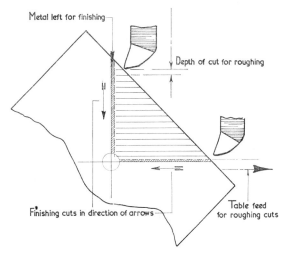

Metal left for finishing

Depth of cut for roughing

Finishing cuts in direction of arrows

Table feed for roughing cuts

FIG. 224.—TECHNIQUE OF ROUGHING AND FINISHING.

It should be clearly understood that the accuracy refers only to the 90° angle, and if this angle is to have accurate linear relationship say to the centre line of the plate, then this accuracy, which is one of alignment, will depend on the precision and skill used in setting the component in the machine vice. In this event, of course, the craftsman will not hesitate to use bevel gauges or a vernier protractor in order to ensure that his setting is as accurate as he can possibly make it. We see then, that with due care and skill in setting the component, together with full use of the geometric movements possessed by the machine tool, it is possible to produce accurate work on a shaping machine, and the example chosen is a very simple one, for the shaping machine is capable of much more versatile work than this.

It is difficult to describe practical work in the pages of a printed book, for there is only one place where practice can be properly learned and that is in the engineering workshop. It is possible, however, as we have

attempted, to give some general guidance in the principles and techniques involved, and the following hints may assist the younger engineer
in his approach to shaping technique.

Best Use of the Vice

Most shaper vices may be rotated or indexed at any particular angle,
and full use should be made of this useful device.

Machining Flats on Round Bars

This is easily done using a shaping machine, and the work may be
held in a pair of V blocks. Shape one side, and check with micrometer
or calipers. Swivel vice through 180°, and shape other side; check with
micrometer or calipers. The technique is illustrated in fig. 225, and the
parallelism of the slots will be dependent on the accuracy of the
indexing of the vice.

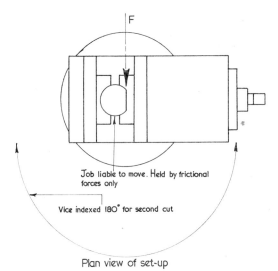

Plan view of set-up

FIG. 225.—INDEXING SHAPER VICE THROUGH 180°.

Reference back to fig. 225, shows that the vice must have its movement parallel to the table movement, if we are to swing through 180°,
and this causes the undesirable feature of poor support for the work, as
the V blocks are now held only by frictional resistance between their
faces and the vice jaws. This is not good machining practice, for a
heavy cut will surely tilt the V blocks in the vice jaws, with the possibility
of damage to both work and V blocks.

Is there not a better way of machining these two parallel faces using a shaping machine? The student is advised to pause here, and give more thought to this problem, and see if he can find the solution.

The answer is simple. Place the job truly vertical in the vice, using the V blocks and tighten. See that the vice faces the cut so that the jaws will take the cutting force. The observant student will notice that the cutting thrust is taken by the sliding member of the vice, but although this may be considered as bad practice, it is unavoidable. A cut is now taken to the scribed line and checked with a micrometer. There is an indexing dial at the hand feed handle of the table movement on most shapers, and this can be used to obtain the required linear movement. On completion of the first face the tool can be replaced with an opposite hand tool, the table moved over, and the machining completed. In this way the sides of the machined flat will be truly parallel. The technique is shown in fig. 226.

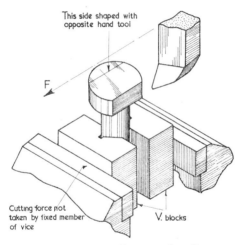

This side shaped with opposite hand tool

F

Cutting force not taken by fixed member of vice

V. blocks

FIG. 226.—SHAPING TWO FLATS IN ONE SETTING.

This principle is widely used for the shaping of components that have several parallel faces, for it is easier to change the tool than to change the setting of the component. Fig. 227 illustrates a typical engineering component machined on a shaper. It is essential that the machined faces on the top surface of the component be parallel, and a high degree of accuracy can be achieved by using one setting of the component, and tool changing. Note how the geometric accuracy of the machined faces is achieved by using the geometric movements embodied in the machine tool.

P

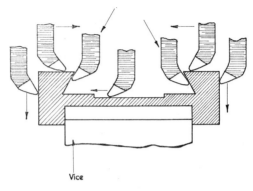

Front elevation

FIG. 227.—SHAPING SEVERAL FACES IN ONE SETTING.

Shaping Tools

The shaping tool is a single-point cutting tool and is usually of a more robust section than a lathe tool. This is due to the fact that the cutting action is not continuous, and the tool is subject to a considerable impact at the commencement of the cut.

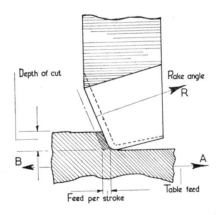

Front elevation

FIG. 228.—OBLIQUE SHAPING TOOL.

Once again the cutting action may be orthogonal or oblique, and the rake angle is of great importance. A typical shaping tool used to generate a plane surface is shown in fig. 228. The rake angle or angle of greatest slope is shown by the arrow R and this has, therefore, an oblique cutting action. It is essential that the minimum length of tool be allowed to protrude below the sliding head, and this sliding head itself should not have excessive movement below its slide.

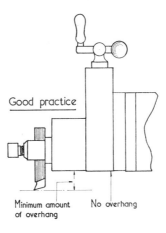

Good practice

Minimum amount   No overhang
of overhang

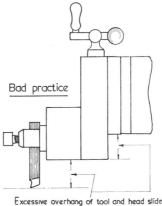

Bad practice

Excessive overhang of tool and head slide

FIG. 229.—IMPORTANCE OF MAXIMUM RIGIDITY.

Examples of bad and good practice are shown in fig. 229. It is also bad practice to take cuts in both directions when using the tool shown in fig. 228. The tool will only have an effective rake when the table is fed in the direction of arrow A, and feeding of the table in direction of arrow B, whilst taking a cut, would result in the tool cutting with a negative rake. Cutting in both directions is only permissible with round nose or finishing tools, and such tools would only be used for light finishing cuts. These are shown in fig. 230, and the amount of metal removal will be small.

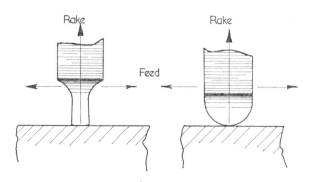

FIG. 230.—SHAPER FINISHING TOOLS.

Summary

Considerable importance has been given to the shaping machine in this chapter. This applies not only to the constructional details of this machine tool, but also to the technique of its operation. With regard to the constructional details, particularly in respect to the methods used in the movement of the ram and the feeding of the table, the student may have observed that the illustrations have, in some cases, assumed an engineering function or character. The purpose of all engineering drawings is to convey information, and this must be done in a clear and concise manner with no possibility of misinterpretation. Any drawing which does not meet these requirements is of little value, and the engineering student is strongly advised to acquire the ability to make neat well proportioned freehand sketches of engineering components. Technicians are often called upon to investigate and solve the multitude of snags and problems that always arise in engineering production, and the ability not only to read, but also to produce engineering drawings, is an essential acomplishment of a first class Technician. Due regard should also be given to the materials used in machine tool construction, and the student will find that ferrous metals have a considerable dominance over non ferrous metals.

We have seen in this chapter some of the capabilities of the shaping machine, when used to best advantage, and this follows the concept of the maximum amount of work for the minimum amount of effort. It is pointless to spend time and energy setting a job **twice** to produce faces at 90°, when provision already exists to machine these faces at 90° in

one setting by using the accurate geometric movements built into the machine tool. The maximum use of the movements on a machine tool is the basis of machining craft, and this applies to all machine tools. The importance of careful study of the component to be machined cannot be overstressed, and the old adage "measure *twice* and cut *once*" is worth remembering. In cases of doubt, the student should not be afraid to ask, for no true engineer would withhold knowledge from another engineer, be he an apprentice or a time served man.

QUESTIONS ON CHAPTER TEN

Part A

1. Show, by means of a simple diagram, the essential movements necessary to generate a plane surface using a shaping machine.

2. Why are shaping machines seldom used on production work?

3. Make a neat front elevation of a simple shaping machine indicating the essential geometry.

4. Show, by means of a sketch, the method of guiding the ram of a shaping machine.

5. What principle is used in the sliding head of a shaping machine?

6. Why is the body of sliding head indexed in angular divisions?

7. What is the purpose of a clapper box on a shaping machine?

8. Make a neat sketch showing a shaping cut that would necessitate tilting of the clapper box.

9. Make a simple diagram showing how automatic table feed is obtained.

10. Why is a shaping machine vice usually of the adjustable rotary type?

11. Why is it necessary to have a stroke adjusting device for the ram movement of a shaping machine?

12. Why is it necessary to adjust the position of a ram? Illustrate, with a sketch of a component to be shaped, the method of positioning of the ram.

13. Why are several different tool shapes required for efficient use of the shaping machine?

14. For what reason are shaper tools of stronger section than lathe tools?

15. Make a neat sketch of a job you would shape in one setting, involving the technique of tool changing.

Part B

1. Make a neat diagram to illustrate the principle of the quick return motion of a shaping machine.

2. Sketch the mechanical device used to change the stroke length.

3. Make a neat sketch of a tool, used to take a downward cut with the head set at 45°. Why is the clapper box set at an angle?

4. Sketch the device used to obtain:
   (i) left hand table movement,
   (ii) right hand table movement,
   (iii) table in the neutral position.

5. The sliding head of a shaping machine has a lead screw of $1/10''$ pitch. If there are five divisions on the indexing dial, what is the linear movement of the tool, if the sliding head handle is indexed three divisions?

Index

Numbers in **bold** type refer to illustrations.